Conquer~ ~hol
Aۥ ۱1

How Alcohol Abuse Is
Gradually Affecting Your
Personality And Life And How
You Can Become Completely
Sober In 3 Weeks

By

Patrick Dickinson

Table of Contents

The Alcohol Myth

The 21-Day Alcohol Switch

The Alcohol Myth

Little-Known Facts About The
Pure Poison That Gradually
Sucks The Life Out Of You

By

Patrick Dickinson

Introduction

Have you ever wondered what you're really putting in your body when you consume an alcoholic beverage? Sure, we all enjoy a drink or two from time to time, but do we realize that even a single alcoholic beverage can cause serious, long-term health damage? Even the short-term effects of alcohol, though they may seem fun and harmless, are extremely dangerous. Long-term alcohol consumption is much 3worse and causes irreversible damage to the kidneys, liver, digestive system, and brain. What's more, alcohol is extremely addictive and can have dramatic effects on the circuitry of the brain. It is very easy to develop an alcohol addiction, and it can happen before you even realize how much you are starting to depend on the drug.

Alcoholism can severely affect your mental and physical health. You will increase your risk of cancer and heart disease and destroy your memory. What's more, it can also lead to financial difficulties and can destroy your relationships with loved ones. Thankfully, an addiction to alcohol can be overcome, and all the help and advice you need can be found right here. If you are worried about how much you are drinking, or suspect that you may have developed an alcohol dependency, this book can help you get your life back on track and reassess your relationship with alcohol. On the other hand, if someone you care about is struggling with alcohol abuse, this book will provide you with all the information you need to support them through this tough time and encourage them to seek the help they need.

Overcoming an alcohol addiction is not easy, but with the right knowledge and support, it can be done. As we learn more about the intricate mechanisms through which alcohol affects our nervous systems, so too do we learn more about how to combat the effects of alcohol and overcome our dependency on the drug. Millions of people have been able to beat alcohol successfully using these methods, and you can too. You can overcome your struggles with alcoholism, get your life back on track, improve your relationships with the people you care about the most, enjoy success at your job, and greatly improve your physical and mental health.

For every day that you consume alcohol, you are delaying feeling the best that you can. You are delaying living up to your full potential, and you are hurting yourself and those around you. There is never going to be a better time to reassess your relationship with alcohol than today, so what are you waiting for?

1. Understanding What Alcohol Really Is

Sure, we've all had a few alcoholic beverages in our lives, and we know how alcohol makes us feel, but do we ACTUALLY know what we're drinking? Do we understand the process behind alcohol production, and how different types of alcohol are created? Wine comes from grapes, beer comes from barley, right? Well, yes, but there's a little more to it than that. Let's take a minute to become familiar with alcohol production, and what alcoholic beverages really are.

So, What Exactly Is Alcohol?

Alcohol is an organic compound composed of carbon, hydrogen, and oxygen elements. There are several different types of alcohol, including isopropyl, methyl, and ethyl alcohol. The differences between alcohol types depend on their chemical composition. However, all alcoholic beverages are made from ethanol, as it is less toxic (but still toxic) than both methanol and isopropyl alcohol [1]. Ethanol is also referred to as ethyl alcohol, grain alcohol, or EtOH. It is produced by the fermentation and distilling of simple sugars, typically from sources such as corn, fruit, wheat, barley, and other grains. The production of ethanol from these sources requires yeast, which facilitates the fermentation of sugar to result in various types of drinkable alcohol. The type of alcohol produced varies depending on where the initial sugar came from and how the alcohol was made.

Although most ethanol is produced for consumption as the world's most popular recreational drug, according to the 2014 Global Drug Survey, it also has other applications. These predominantly include roles in the medical field, but also extend across many different kinds of manufacturing industries. However, the amount of ethanol that is produced for these uses pales in comparison to the amount that is consumed by people all over the world, every day, in the form of alcoholic beverages.

What's Really In An Alcoholic Beverage?

An alcoholic drink, or alcoholic beverage, is a drink that contains any amount of ethanol. Beer, wine, and liquor are all common forms of alcoholic beverages, but the list is much longer than this. Different types of alcoholic drinks typically range in alcohol content between 3% and 50%. These beverages are consumed all over the world and play an essential social role in many cultures. Most countries have laws regarding the production, sale, and consumption of alcoholic beverages, with some being stricter than others.

In 2018, the global alcoholic drink industry exceeded $1 trillion. Why is this such a huge industry? Why is alcohol so popular? There are a number of reasons, but the main reason for the global popularity of alcohol is that people like how it makes them feel. Alcohol is a depressant of the central nervous system, and in low doses causes feelings of euphoria, reduced anxiety, and improved self-confidence [2]. In high doses, alcohol may cause drunkenness, stupor, loss of consciousness, and can even result in death [3].

Most people love the way drinking alcohol makes them feel, at least in the short term. Going out and having a few beers doesn't hurt anyone, right? Well, not exactly. Long-term consumption of alcohol can lead to liver disease [4], kidney disease [5], and numerous cancers [6], just to name a few. What's worse, you don't have to be getting blind drunk every night to be experiencing the negative health effects of alcohol. Alcohol is a highly addictive substance that corrupts our neuronal pathways and re-wires our brain. This makes us more and more dependent on the drug that is slowly taking over our lives and killing us.

Just How Popular Is Alcohol?

Despite knowing that alcohol is not suitable for us, around 33% of adults worldwide consume the drug. This makes alcohol one of the most widely used recreational drugs in the world. As of 2016, women were reported to consume 0.7 alcoholic drinks per day, while men consume approximately 1.7. In a 2015 survey among Americans, 86% of adults reported that they had consumed alcohol at some point in time, and 70% had consumed alcohol in the last year. 56% of respondents reported consuming alcohol in the month prior to the survey. You only have to go to a crowded bar on a Saturday night to see just how popular alcohol is.

Exploring The Other Uses Of Alcohol

While most alcohol is produced for human consumption, there are alternative uses for alcohol that have come about over time. As more has been learned about the properties of ethanol, more has been learned about how it can be utilized. Examples of these uses include the following:

Medical And Scientific Uses

Ethanol has wide applications throughout the medical field. It is predominantly used as an antiseptic and disinfectant in hospitals and other medical facilities. Before surgical procedures or immunizations, instruments and areas of the skin that will be pierced are cleaned with an alcohol swab that usually contains 70% ethanol. This provides the highest level of efficacy in removing bacteria and other pathogens, thus keeping wounds and equipment sterile.

70% ethanol spray bottles are found on the benches of every biological laboratory and are used to decontaminate and disinfect workstations on a daily basis. For scientists culturing cells, or working with microbes, contamination can be a huge problem. Ethanol plays an important role in ensuring that work areas stay sterile and free of any contaminants. Other scientific uses for alcohol include a solvent during chemical analyses or in the synthesis of other organic compounds. Ethanol is also used throughout manufacturing industries. Ethanol is also used as a "low-temperature liquid" – the freezing point of ethanol is -173.50F, which means it stays in liquid form at very cold temperatures. In laboratories, "ethanol baths" are used to keep reagents or equipment at very low temperatures.

Ethanol As A Clean-Burning Fuel Source

There has been a dramatic increase in ethanol fuel production over the last decade, with ethanol becoming a popular biofuel additive for gasoline. Ethanol that is produced for biofuel is commonly made from biomass, such as corn or sugarcane. There is a great supply of these types of sugars (typically from agricultural feedstocks), and the procedure of ethanol production is relatively simple and cheap. Today, ethanol-blended fuel is widely used throughout the United States and Europe, with most modern cars able to run on blends of up to 10% ethanol.

Despite these alternatives, widespread uses of ethanol, a vast majority of ethanol production is created for human consumption – beer, wine, and liquor.

Understanding The Different Types Of Alcoholic Drinks

Typically, alcoholic beverages are divided into three categories – beer, wine, and spirits. This is somewhat of an oversimplification because there are other types of alcoholic drinks that don't really fit into these categories. Here, we will discuss some of the main types of alcohol and how they are made.

Beer

Beer is one of the most popular alcoholic beverages in the world and is produced from fermented grain mash. Most beers are made from malted barley, or a blend of several grains (including wheat) to create different flavor profiles. Hops are also often added for additional taste, and has rapidly increased over the last decade or so as the craft beer industry has become increasingly popular. Beer styles such as Indian Pale Ales (IPAs) are loaded with hops to create a darker, heavier beer that typically also contains more alcohol.

With more and more of a demand for craft beers, more styles have emerged in popularity – it's not just ale, lager or pilsner anymore! Beers containing fruit or fruit flavorings have become increasingly common, as have sour beers and a style called gose – a tangy beer with a slightly salty flavor. Many of these beers have been created in an effort to entice individuals who don't normally drink or enjoy beer, by masking the traditional flavor of beer with other ingredients. Typically, the alcohol content of beer ranges from around 3% for a light beer, to up to 12% for a very dark beer, or one that has been barrel-aged. The most common beers contain between 5% and 7% alcohol.

Wine

The wine typically contains 12% to 15% alcohol, though certain varieties may be higher or lower than that. Wine is made from the fermentation of fresh grape juice, and is traditionally available as either "red wine" or "white wine," the latter usually being served chilled. Fruit wines are wines that are made from other types of fruit, such as plums, cherries, or apples, and are not considered traditional wines. Similarly, Sake (popular throughout Japan and now across the world) is referred to as a "rice wine," but is not made from grapes. Red wine is red because some of the grape skin is incorporated into the production process, whereas this does not occur in the production of white wine.

As well as red and white wines, rosé has become a popular option in recent years. This wine tends to be a pinky-orangey color, as some of the grape skin is incorporated, but not enough for the wine to be considered a traditional red wine. Most rosé wines, like white wines, tend to be served chilled, whereas a vast majority of red wines are traditionally served at room temperature. Sparkling wine is another common variety and is made using secondary fermentation. Many people call all sparkling wine Champagne, but this is only correct if the wine comes from the French region Champagne and is produced following a specific set of guidelines.

Cider

Cider is a fermented alcoholic drink made from any type of fruit juice, with apple being the most common and traditional variety of cider. Other common flavors include pears (sometimes referred to as "Perry" cider), peaches, berries, and more. The alcohol content of cider ranges from 1.5% to up to 8% or even higher. Cider is typically less carbonated than beer and can be sweet or "dry" – a tart alternative. Cider is commonly consumed by people who don't like the taste of beer. There are also a large number of non-alcoholic ciders on the market.

Mead

Mead is an alcoholic beverage that is made by fermenting honey with water. Sometimes, mead includes the addition of various fruits, spices, grains, or hops. Mead is less common than beer or wine today but was a popular drink as far back as medieval times. During this time, mead was produced crudely using spices, grain mash, or fruits. Mead was also consumed throughout ancient Europe, Asia, and Africa. The alcohol content of mead varies greatly, from around 8% to over 20%. Mead has quite a distinct flavor, as a majority of the drink's fermentable sugar is derived from honey.

Pulque

Pulque is also known as octli and is an alcoholic drink made from the fermented sap of the agave plant. Pulque is very popular throughout South America, has a milky appearance and a somewhat viscous consistency. Pulque has a sour, yeast-like flavor, and is not at all similar to mezcal, which is made from the cooked heart of certain agave plants. Likewise, pulque offers no similarity to tequila, a variety of mezcal made entirely or predominantly from the blue agave. Pulque has dropped in popularity since the 20th century, with many consumers turning to beer instead.

Liquor

All of the alcoholic beverages described above are produced using fermentation. Liquors (also known as spirits), on the other hand, are produced by distilling grains, fruits, or vegetables that have already been through the alcoholic fermentation process. The process of distilling purifies the liquid, and removes water and other diluting factors, resulting in much more concentrated alcohol. This is why liquor drinks typically have a significantly higher alcohol content than beverages produced via fermentation, such as beer or wine. Examples of liquor include vodka, gin, rum, tequila, baijiu, mezcal and whiskey, and alcohol content of liquors typically exceeds 35%.

As you can see, alcoholic beverages come in a variety of shapes and forms, designed to appeal to everyone. Some people are quite particular about what they drink, having their favorite classic cocktail or go-to beer, while others are less fussy and will drink almost anything. Ultimately, most people are drinking alcohol because of how it makes them feel, rather than how it tastes.

2. Understanding The Negative Effects That Alcohol Can Have On Your Life

Drinking the occasional alcoholic beverage might seem harmless enough, but alcohol can have huge effects on our bodies and our minds. Alcohol is highly addictive and can be deadly if abused in the long-term. Though it is a very complicated science, we now have an extensive understanding of how alcohol hijacks the reward pathways of the brain and leads to addiction and abuse of the drug.

How Alcohol Addiction Works

Alcohol can encourage us to behave in ways that we may not always be proud of. By removing our inhibitions, even just a small amount of alcohol can make us act out of character. Although alcohol is a depressant, the immediate effects of alcohol are to enhance our self-confidence, improve our mood, and make us more social, among other things. One of the major effects of alcohol consumption is that it can increase the likelihood that we will undertake "risk-taking" behaviors and questionable decision making. Examples may include feeling as though we are fine to drive home after an evening at the bar, or engaging in high-risk sexual situations.

Alcohol can also be appealing for its ability to distract ourselves from aspects of our day-to-day life that we may wish to escape. Whether it is a general feeling of sadness or dissatisfaction with life, or an emotional issue such as a relationship break up, alcohol can help us forget the things that make life difficult. One of the major problems that comes with using alcohol in this way is that we forget how to deal with some of the more challenging aspects of life, and lose some of our natural coping mechanisms. Some people turn to alcohol as a method for dealing with the many ups and downs that are a natural part of life. Although alcohol may feel like an effective solution in the short term, it makes things far worse in the long run.

When we drink alcohol, many changes begin to occur within our brains via the effects of neurotransmitters, including dopamine, serotonin, and gamma-Aminobutyric acid (GABA). Neurotransmitters are chemicals produced by the body that are released at the end of a nerve fiber to impact a target neuron, muscle, or gland. Alcohol interacts with numerous neurotransmitters in the brain, either up-regulating or down-regulating their levels. This can have drastic effects on our mood and behavior.

In a study investigating the effects of alcohol intake on mice, researchers found that alcohol consumption significantly increased levels of the neurotransmitter GABA in the brain [7]. GABA plays a range of roles in the brain, including reducing levels of stress, anxiety, depression, and pain [8]. When we drink alcohol, our GABA levels increase, and our feelings of stress and anxiety are reduced. This is one of the reasons why drinking feels so good, and why our brains are programmed to enjoy it and to want to keep doing it.

Another study on mice showed that immediately after alcohol consumption, dopamine is released in the brain [9]. Dopamine is a neurotransmitter that has been highly implicated in addiction and reward systems. When we do something, our brain thinks it is good for us, like taking a drink of water when we're thirsty, our brain releases dopamine to act as a "reward." Dopamine release results in feelings of pleasure and is designed to act as positive reinforcement. This means that when we do something that is considered good for us, our brain wants to make sure we continue to do it [10]. We like the way dopamine makes us feel, so we will continue to perform behaviors that result in a dopamine release.

Alcohol addiction works primarily through the dopamine release system, and in fact, hijacks the dopamine pathway. Alcohol consumption results in a dopamine boost that's usually significantly stronger than the amount our brain would normally release

[11]. Before too long, our brains start to associate alcohol consumption with feelings of pleasure, which forms the basis for alcohol abuse and addiction. These hijacked pathways become strengthened and reinforced over time, resulting in alcohol cravings or dependencies. It is a very strong pathway, and a very difficult cycle to break.

One of the reasons why this cycle is so toxic is that with time, more and more alcohol is required to deliver the same degree of dopamine release. Initially, a dopamine release may occur after just a drink or two. However, once the neuronal pathway has been established, and the pleasure centers of the brain are corrupted, substantially more alcohol is required to deliver a feeling of pleasure. Constantly giving into cravings for alcohol and feeding this dopamine release is what leads to a true alcohol addiction. In essence, it is not the alcohol itself we are craving. Many individuals suffering from alcoholism no longer enjoy the taste of alcohol, or enjoy drinking, or even really notice that they are doing it.

What is causing the addiction is not the alcohol, but the dopamine itself.

Once the alcohol starts affecting an individual's ability to work, or their relationships with friends or family, it can be considered an addiction rather than just a habit. People with this level of alcohol dependency are not easily able to give up alcohol, and attempting to do so often results in an alcohol withdrawal syndrome. Depending on how much alcohol an individual was consuming, the symptoms of alcohol withdrawal may include sweating, nausea, shakiness, anxiety, and headaches. In more severe cases, withdrawal results in delirium tremens, which can include hallucinating, uncontrollable shaking, and mental confusion, and can even be deadly [12].

Once this level of alcohol addiction has been established, it is very hard to stop drinking. For many people, by the time they realize they are addicted to alcohol, it is too late to break the cycle. Complete and successful alcohol detoxification for an established addict requires medical assistance. This type of treatment is usually performed in a designated facility under strict supervision. Even after detoxification, the effects of alcohol on the brain are so strong that relapse is always a possibility. For this reason, many people who have previously had an alcohol dependency are rarely able to return to a "safe" level of social drinking. Instead, these individuals usually must remain completely sober.

Alcohol can have seriously profound effects on both physical and mental health and is responsible for contributing to a wide range of severe ailments and illnesses. The effects of alcohol worsen as the number of alcohol increases, and there is no safe lower limit of alcohol – even a single drink can cause harm. The most common short and long-term health effects of alcohol are outlined and explained below. This is by no means an extensive list, as new links between alcohol and disease are continuing to be established, and different individuals may be affected differently by alcohol consumption.

What Are The Short-Term Effects Of Alcohol Consumption?

Many people find that feeling the short-term effects of alcohol consumption can be quite an enjoyable experience. In the short-term, alcohol consumption can have a wide range of effects, mostly affecting our brains. This is because, unlike most substances, alcohol can cross the blood-brain-barrier, allowing it to move from our bloodstream to our brain cells (neurons). The blood-brain-barrier is in place to protect our sensitive neurons from potentially harmful substances that may be circulating in our bloodstream. Unfortunately, there is no protection in place against alcohol, leaving our brains wide open to the effects of the drug [13].

One of the earliest and most common short-term

effects of alcohol consumption is a sense of decreased anxiety [14]. Many people take advantage of this and use alcohol as an icebreaker, or to improve their confidence in new or challenging social situations. For individuals with social anxiety, alcohol provides a way in which they feel confident enough to interact with others. However, alcohol consumption actually increases anxiety in the long-term and should not be used as a method of reducing anxiety. If you're looking for a natural method of reducing anxiety, try increasing your levels of physical activity instead.

Another short-term effect of alcohol consumption is a decrease in motor skill function. This is commonly associated with alcohol intoxication and is the reason why certain sobriety tests may include motor functions like walking in a straight line or testing your ability to balance. The cerebellum of the brain works with the primary motor cortex to control movement, balance, and carry out complex motor functions. Alcohol consumption affects the neurons of the cerebellum, impairing their ability to function

[15]. Intoxicated individuals often don't realize how impaired their motor function is, which can be particularly dangerous if, for example, they try to drive.

Along with decreased motor function and reduced anxiety, another short-term effect of alcohol consumption is euphoria. This is due to the aforementioned effects that alcohol has on the reward pathways of the brain. It is not the alcohol itself that is resulting in feelings of euphoria and pleasure. It is the dopamine that our brain releases to thank us for the alcohol. Many people come to crave this feeling, say, after a long day at work. The initial feelings of euphoria that come with alcohol may be why that first sip on a Friday afternoon always tastes so good.

The above short-term effects of alcohol are all seen when low doses of alcohol are ingested. If the amount of alcohol consumed is higher, the effects of the drug can be much more drastic. For example, high doses of alcohol can cause anterograde amnesia, which is where the brain is unable to form new memories [16]. This is why you may not remember a night of heavy drinking, and is also referred to as "blacking out". All those embarrassing things definitely did happen, but the alcohol blocked the neural pathways in the brain that are responsible for forming new memories. The scary thing is that this isn't something that only occurs after years of alcohol abuse. In fact, just one night of drinking can cause anterograde amnesia and seriously affect your brain's ability to form memories.

Other short-term effects of high-dose alcohol consumption can be much more serious than memory loss. Even just short-term abuse of alcohol can result in unconsciousness or even death if the amount of alcohol consumed is high enough. Unfortunately, the cell membranes that protect each and every cell in our body are highly permeable to alcohol. This means that it is taken up into almost any cell; it comes into contact with once it enters our bloodstream. Therefore, the effects of alcohol can be so systemic, or widespread, and pronounced.

Understanding The Long-Term Effects Of Alcohol Consumption

While it is true that alcohol consumption is damaging in the short-term, the toxic effects of the drug are even more pronounced if alcohol is consumed on a long-term basis. In the past, there have been studies suggesting that small amounts of certain types of alcoholic drinks (such as a glass of red wine twice a week) can actually improve health. However, more recent, meta-analyses of the data do not echo this result. What's more, any positive effects of red wine (or other types of alcohol) on our health are likely caused by other ingredients in the wine despite the alcohol content, rather than because of it.

The long-term effects of alcohol consumption can be

dire, particularly if alcohol is consumed in excess for many years. Heavy consumption of alcohol, or alcohol abuse, can cause serious detrimental and irreversible health problems. These may include alcoholic liver disease, cancer, heart disease, chronic pancreatitis, malnutrition, damage to the central and peripheral nervous systems, and so much more. Even light to moderate alcohol consumption can increase the risk of certain cancers – there is no safe amount when it comes to alcohol consumption. The effects of alcohol are felt systemically, all over the body, and may even be experienced for years after an individual stops drinking. The vital biological systems most commonly affected by alcohol consumption are outlined below.

How Alcohol Affects The Nervous System

Our nervous system is one of the most important parts of our body. Our central nervous system (brain and spinal cord) connects with our peripheral nervous system (nerve fibers located peripherally all over our skin and internal organs). Together, the various components of the nervous system help us sense, respond, interpret, move, think, and feel. The correct functioning of the nervous system is crucial to our survival as humans. We must be able to learn, think, create memories, feel pain, run, and do all the other things our brain handles. There are so many diseases of the nervous system, and they all have devastating effects – Alzheimer's Disease affects our memory, Parkinson's Disease affects our motor skills, just to name two. Alcohol, too, can have hugely devastating and irreversible effects on the nervous system. Specific brain regions appear more susceptible than others to the effects of alcohol, including the prefrontal cortex, the amygdala, and the hypothalamus.

For neurons (one type of cell found in the nervous system) to communicate with each other, a release of chemicals called neurotransmitters is required. One neuron will release neurotransmitters at what is called a synapse, or a meeting of two neurons. On the other side of the synapse, the second neuron will sense and take up the released neurotransmitter, resulting in downstream signaling. This signaling may involve the release of hormones, or activation of muscle cells if a movement is to be performed. Alcohol can greatly affect the levels of various neurotransmitters within the brain, which wreaks chaos on the regular nervous system function. This can affect our mood, hormone levels, appetite, and so many other days to day feelings and functions.

In addition, chronic heavy alcohol consumption can severely impair brain development [17]. This is why alcohol is particularly dangerous for teens and adolescents and can result in serious long-term problems. In particular, alcohol can severely impair learning and memory in teens, as this is a critical period of development where the brain is making progress towards maturity. During this time, the brain is making improvements in decision-making functions and associated connections with the memory regions of the brain. These changes last through the teenage years and into an individual's early 20s – covering the periods of time when an individual is most likely to begin to use and abuse alcohol.

As well as causing irreversible damage to teen brains, alcohol can have a range of horrific effects on the brains of adults. Alcohol has been shown to cause shrinkage of the brain (neural atrophy) and alcoholic polyneuropathy, a degenerative disorder of the peripheral nerves that results in weakness and pain. What's more, alcohol increases the risk of developing neuropsychiatric and cognitive disorders and distorts brain chemistry.

At present, the literature is inconclusive regarding links between alcohol consumption and dementia risk. There is some evidence to suggest that low to moderate alcohol consumption may decrease the risk of developing dementia [18]. However, there are also some studies refuting this, finding no protective effect of alcohol consumption for dementia risk. What's more, the protective effect of "alcohol" may actually be caused by different ingredients in alcoholic drinks (such as vitamins and flavonoids in red wine), rather than the alcohol itself.

The Effects Of Alcohol On The Cardiovascular System

Our cardiovascular system is made up of our heart and blood vessels and is responsible for pumping blood all around our bodies. This helps to nourish muscles and remove waste products as they build up. The importance of "heart-health" cannot be overstated, with heart disease and heart attacks both being increasingly prevalent causes of death in the 21st century. Alcohol can have a wide range of effects on cardiovascular health, both in the short and long term. Short-term effects of alcohol consumption on the cardiovascular system include an increased heart rate and increased blood pressure. For individuals with a heart condition, this can be highly dangerous and even lead to a stroke.

Long-term consumption of alcohol results in even more detrimental effects on the cardiovascular system, including cardiomyopathy, or damage to the heart muscle itself [19]. Cardiomyopathy results in weakened heart muscle that, in turn, causes the four chambers of the heart to become enlarged. This results in weaker contractions, or heartbeats, making it harder for the heart to circulate blood around the body. The heart has to work harder, and the extra strain put on the muscle can eventually lead to congestive heart failure.

In addition, alcohol can cause irregular heartbeats or arrhythmias. Arrhythmias can be lethal if undiagnosed and may go on to cause cardiac arrest or stroke. Atrial fibrillation is a relatively common arrhythmia that causes the upper chambers of the heart to quiver rather than beat normally. Staggeringly, alcohol has been shown to cause atrial fibrillation after just one drinking session [20]. What's more, the effects alcohol has on atrial fibrillation are compounded over time, putting excess strain on the heart. When the heart cannot pump blood as effectively as it should be, blood pools in the upper chambers of the heart and may clot. If these clots break off and become lodged in an artery within the brain, they can easily cause an ischemic stroke.

Alcohol also increases your risk of a heart attack. Typically, alcohol consumption raises the levels of fats in the bloodstream. These increased triglyceride levels often coincide with high levels of "bad" cholesterol, which can all combine to result in the clogging of arteries due to the build-up of plaque, fat, and cholesterol. This can restrict or cut off blood flow through a coronary artery, which in turn can cause a heart attack. Alcohol consumption also increases your risk of both ischemic and hemorrhagic stroke, rounding out a long list of detrimental cardiovascular effects.

Effects Of Alcohol On Digestion

In general, alcohol irritates the digestive system. Even a small amount of alcohol can increase stomach acid production, which can, in turn, cause gastritis – the inflammation of the stomach lining. This may cause stomach pain, vomiting, diarrhea, and even bleeding in heavy drinkers. Long term alcohol abuse can have additional and much more serious effects on the digestive system. Such effects may include an increased predisposition to cancer of the mouth, throat, stomach, and colon. Additionally, peptic ulcer risk increases – this is a painful, open sore in the lining of your stomach.

Excessive alcohol consumption can also cause vomiting, usually as your body tries to remove as much of the drug as possible from your system. Vomiting can be very dangerous if you are unconscious, with the potential for choking or aspirating. Violent vomiting can also tear the lining of the throat, resulting in the vomiting of blood and a bleed in the upper digestive system, which can be life-threatening if not treated. What's more, the acidity of vomit is very bad for your throat, mouth, and teeth, and has been linked with peptic ulcers as well as an increased risk of throat or mouth cancer.

Long-term, chronic alcoholism can also result in severe malnutrition, and even consuming lower levels of alcohol can have some negative effects on nutrient absorption [21]. Alcohol interrupts the breakdown of nutrients by decreasing digestive enzymes produced by the pancreas. Alcohol also affects the absorption of these nutrients by damaging the cells lining the stomach and intestines. This means that vital nutrients from our foods can't be transported from the stomach to the bloodstream, and our cells don't get the nourishment they need. Even if you are eating a nutrient-rich, healthy diet, the consumption of alcohol alongside with this diet negates a majority of the health benefits. This means that you are missing out on many of the nutrients on offer, as your body cannot absorb and utilize them.

Effects Of Alcohol On The Liver And Pancreas

The liver is one of the organs that are most closely associated with alcohol consumption. Our liver is responsible for metabolizing over 90% of dietary alcohol, as well as other harmful substances in the blood. As many as 20% of heavy drinkers develop fatty liver disease – a relatively symptomless condition that marks the initial loss of liver function. Excess fat builds up in the liver, thereby decreasing liver function. Chronic alcohol abuse causes the destruction of liver cells, which in turn causes scarring of the liver known as cirrhosis. In addition, liver inflammation, known as alcoholic hepatitis, may occur, as well as cellular mutations that can ultimately result in liver cancer.

Alcohol can have similarly drastic effects on the pancreas. Heavy alcohol consumption is associated with pancreatitis – inflammation of the pancreas that is very painful and can be potentially fatal. The cells of the pancreas convert alcohol into toxic byproducts that cause damage to the ducts of the pancreas. Enzymes that are normally released into the digestive tract can't be released, and instead build up and begin to digest the pancreas itself. Around one in three cases of acute pancreatitis in the United States is caused by alcohol. This condition is characterized by severe abdominal and back pain, jaundice, a low-grade fever, nausea or vomiting, and loss of appetite. Repeated cases of acute pancreatitis cause irreversible damage to the pancreas, resulting in chronic pancreatitis, which can also lead to diabetes.

How Alcohol Affects The Immune System

The effects of alcohol on the immune system are complex and not fully understood. Chronic alcohol abuse leads to a weakened immune system and increases the chances of developing an opportunistic or other infection [22]. However, the reasons for this are not entirely understood. One important factor is thought to be the gut microbiome, which has already been shown to play an important role in fighting infection. Alcohol consumption severely disturbs the gut microbiome, disrupting the balance between healthy and unhealthy gut bacteria. Alcohol also affects the way gut microbes interact with the immune system and disrupts the gut barrier, which allows more bacteria to enter into the bloodstream.

Studies have also shown that excessive alcohol consumption can reduce the number and function of three crucial types of immune cells – macrophages, B lymphocytes, and T lymphocytes. These cells are all responsible for fighting diseases, infections, and would-be invading pathogens. Macrophages are the first line of defense for the immune system, attacking pathogens as soon as they are discovered. Lymphocytes act as the memory of the immune system, recognizing an infection before it has a chance to become established in the body. With fewer immune cells circulating in the blood, your body is more open and exposed to potential pathogens. This increases your likelihood of catching a virus or decreasing your ability to recognize foreign cancer cells.

It's not just the above systems that are affected by alcohol consumption - the respiratory system, kidneys, reproductive system, endocrine system, bones, and skin can all also be affected. In short, there isn't a single organ, tissue, or cell in our body that doesn't feel the toxic effects of alcohol.

3. Understanding The Mechanisms Behind Alcohol Addiction

For many adults, light to moderate drinking isn't a major health concern, or a priority when it comes to making lifestyle changes. We may occasionally think we should cut back (usually after a night involving one too many drinks), but most of us don't get around to it, or if we do, it's only for a week or so. However, it's important to realize that alcohol addiction doesn't occur overnight – it is a process, and results from the long-term abuse of alcohol. If you feel as though you are drinking too much at once, or drinking too regularly, alcohol addiction may already be taking over your life.

Alcohol addiction, or alcoholism, is a disease that can affect anyone at any time. Certain individuals may be more predisposed than others to develop the disease, but alcohol is a highly addictive and toxic drug that does not discriminate when it comes to who can and can't get addicted. Genetics, gender, race, and socioeconomics can all play a role in determining how likely someone is to abuse alcohol. Still, there is no single cause of alcoholism and no real way of knowing who it will affect.

While some people still hold the antiquated view that addiction is a sign of weakness, it is important to realize that alcohol addiction is a very real and serious disease. Alcoholism changes the brain and its associated neurochemistry, meaning that a person with an addiction to alcohol may not be able to control their behavior or actions. The toxic condition is not something that simply resolves itself over time, and external intervention is most often required to try to free someone from the grips of alcoholism.

We know that alcoholism is difficult to beat due to the deadly feedback loop that is caused by dopamine and the pleasure centers of the brain. With enough time, the brain begins to rely on alcohol to keep dopamine levels high, making it nearly impossible to give up alcohol. So, we know why it can be hard to beat alcohol addiction, but what actually causes somebody to become addicted to alcohol in the first place? Well, the short answer is that it's different for everyone, but there are a certain set of factors that seem to play a role in almost every case of alcoholism.

How Biological Factors Can Lead To Alcoholism

One of the key biological factors that affect the development of alcoholism is genetics. In recent years, a growing body of evidence has led to the suggestion that alcoholism is genetic. However, this is complicated by the vast number of genes that appear to play a part in determining the risk of alcoholism. In short, there is certainly a key genetic component to alcoholism, but there is no single "alcoholic gene" that triples your risk of developing alcoholism, for example. Instead, the genetic component of alcoholism is a complex interplay between a large number of genes, with more and more genes being implicated in alcohol and drug addiction pathways each year.

Two of the genes with the strongest known effects on alcoholism risk are both involved in the metabolism of alcohol. Those genes are alcohol dehydrogenase 1B (*ADH1B*) and alcohol dehydrogenase 2 (*ALDH2*). These genes are partially responsible for producing alcohol dehydrogenase, an enzyme that is crucial for the liver when metabolizing alcohol [23]. Certain variants of these genes that are extremely prevalent throughout Asian populations prevents the proper metabolism of alcohol. This causes a buildup of toxic intermediate substances such as acetaldehyde and results in dizziness, nausea, and tachycardia. The symptoms are severe enough to deter most individuals with this genetic variant from consuming alcohol; thus, they are somewhat genetically protected against developing alcoholism.

Scientists have also identified genes that play a role in determining how likely an individual is to develop an addiction. There's certainly evidence to suggest that some individuals are genetically predisposed to develop an addiction, just as some individuals are more likely to develop cancer than others because of a genetic variant. One of the genes that have been implicated in addiction is the mu-opioid receptor (OPRM1) gene. This gene produces a protein that a certain neurotransmitter binds to, resulting in a pleasurable endorphin release in the brain.

Certain individuals have a genetic variant of the gene that results in the protein having a much stronger affinity for the neurotransmitter. In this case, when the neurotransmitter (released in response to alcohol) binds to the protein, the pleasurable endorphin release is much stronger than other individual's experiences. This means that the "reward" for drinking alcohol is much higher in those individuals; thus, they are more likely to do it again [24]. Many so-called "addiction genes" exist that operate in a similar manner to this.

The Role Of Environmental Factors In Alcoholism

There are many environmental factors that can play a role in determining whether or not an individual is at increased risk of developing alcoholism. Although not solely responsible for causing alcoholism, our environment can play a large role in determining the health of our relationship with alcohol. Alarmingly, the environment in which a child is raised can play a significant role in whether or not they develop alcoholism later in life.

Studies have shown that individuals who grow up in a family where one or more individuals drink heavily are more likely to abuse alcohol themselves [25]. Sometimes, these individuals abuse alcohol to cope with their living situations and problems they are already experiencing. It is a vicious cycle of alcohol abuse that can be passed down through the generations if the cycle is not broken. For others, they see other members of their family normalizing alcohol abuse, and are therefore more likely to view this as acceptable behavior and develop a similarly unhealthy relationship with alcohol. In some cases, alcohol consumption is even glamorized, making it seem more socially acceptable and desirable.

A person's income level can also play a role in their relationship with alcohol. A recent study showed that there was more variation in how much individuals with lower incomes drank compared to those with higher incomes [26]. The low-income group contained more light drinkers and non-drinkers, as well as more heavy drinkers than the high-income group. People in the high-income group were more likely to drink overall, but also more likely to moderate their alcohol intake. This suggests that these individuals were more likely to have a healthier relationship with alcohol.

In addition, the cost of alcohol and the ease with which it can be obtained seem to play a role in alcoholism. In areas where alcohol is heavily taxed and very expensive, fewer individuals develop alcoholism. Similarly, when alcohol cannot be easily obtained and where laws regarding alcohol consumption are stricter, individuals are less likely to develop alcoholism. Overall, the more pervasive the presence of alcohol is in a given environment, the higher the chances of individuals within that environment developing alcoholism.

Psychological Factors That May Cause Alcoholism

There are numerous psychological factors that can play a role in determining how likely an individual is to develop alcoholism. Individuals who suffer from depression, bipolar disorder, or social anxiety all have a higher risk of developing alcoholism when compared to those who don't suffer from these conditions. It is estimated that around 40% of individuals suffering from bipolar disorder are dependent on alcohol, and around 20% of individuals suffering from depression are dependent on alcohol.

Many individuals experiencing mental health problems turn to alcohol in an attempt to self-medicate and find some relief from the conditions they are suffering from. For example, individuals with schizophrenia often use alcohol to "quiet" the voices in their head and help them feel more relaxed and grounded. Similarly, individuals with depression believe that alcohol can improve their mood and make them feel happier. Alcohol may be an effective method of self-medication for these individuals in the short-term, due to the feelings of euphoria that come from the drug. However, in the long-term, alcohol causes depression, worsening the mental health of the individuals trying to self-medicate with the drug.

Self-medicating with alcohol is particularly common among individuals who have not actually been diagnosed with a mental health disorder, or who may be avoiding medical treatment when they suspect they have a condition. Similarly, individuals who seek treatment and are prescribed medication often turn to alcohol instead, as certain medications for mental health conditions can cause unwanted side effects. Many medications prescribed for mental health conditions can take several months to start working properly, and it can be difficult to find the right combination of prescription drugs for certain patients. Individuals often turn to alcohol as a "quick-fix" rather than waiting to see results using actual-prescribed drugs.

Although self-medicating with alcohol may be tempting, it is not recommended as it does not solve the underlying mental health problems. Ultimately, these issues need addressing with therapy and/or prescription medication. What's more, although long-term use of certain prescription drugs can be tough on your kidneys and liver, long-term use of alcohol is far worse and can cause a whole host of additional health issues. Using alcohol to self-medicate commonly leads to alcohol abuse and addiction, as more and more alcohol is required to have a therapeutic effect.

How Social Factors Play A Role In The Development Of Alcoholism

Social, cultural, and religious factors can all play a role in the development of alcoholism. Although it is possible for individuals of any religion to abuse alcohol, alcoholism and alcohol abuse are seen far less frequently in religions where alcohol consumption is strongly opposed or limited. This effect is compounded when the religion in question has a strong influence on local laws, social practices, and how easily alcohol can be obtained. Examples of such religions include Islam, Mormonism, Orthodox Judaism, and Evangelical Protestantism.

In addition to religion, many social and cultural factors can influence an individual's likelihood of developing alcoholism. Typically, individuals who are in social situations where drinking alcohol is widely accepted, or even encouraged, are more likely to abuse alcohol. One such example is college – although a majority of college students work hard, there's no denying that in many social circles, college students also consume a lot of alcohol. Many college students find themselves in situations with free-flowing alcohol, and there is undoubtedly a culture among students where drinking is accepted and even encouraged.

One danger of such situations is the effect that peer pressure can have, particularly on young and highly impressionable college-aged individuals. In many cases, students are meeting potential new friends, classmates and roommates, and people who they may need to spend the next several years with. For this reason, many people are looking to make good first impressions, and will often do whatever is needed to fit in. This often results in excessive alcohol consumption and the resulting in potentially risky behaviors. Such situations can be especially risky for young female students, who often end up in unwanted and risky sexual situations following excessive alcohol intake [27].

The binge-drinking culture that has been extensively studied throughout college students is particularly concerning given the brain development that is still occurring among these individuals. What's more, college-aged students are at the age when they are most susceptible to developing alcoholism. It has been widely established that alcohol use most commonly begins in the late teen years to the early twenties when most individuals start drinking. With teens exposed to so much alcohol so quickly, it is difficult for them to establish healthy drinking habits or a "normal" relationship with alcohol.

As you can see, there are a vast number of factors that can contribute to alcohol use and abuse. Importantly, it must be realized that no individual is immune to developing alcoholism, and each individual with alcohol use disorder took a different path to get there. There are many different types of alcohol abuse, and alcoholism can affect different individuals in different ways, as will be described in the next chapter.

4. The Drastic Effects Alcohol Can Have On Behavior, Personality, And Lifestyle

A recent study conducted through the National Institute on Alcohol Abuse and Alcoholism (NIAAA), the National Institute of Health (NIH) and the National Epidemiological Survey on Alcohol and Related Conditions (NESARC) examined the different types of alcoholism. These organizations conducted a national, clinical study derived from various studies on the different types of alcoholism. Today, it is widely accepted that there are five broad sub-types of alcoholism, with some overlap between different subtypes. Let's take a look at each subtype, and how each differs from the next.

The Five Broad Subtypes Of Alcoholics

Young Adult Subtype

The young adult subtype is the largest of each of the groups, which accounts for just under one-third of all individuals suffering from alcoholism in the United States. Typically, this group of individuals aged in their late teens through to early 20s – many of these individuals are not even old enough to legally drink yet! Perhaps unsurprisingly, a large number of individuals in this category are college students, who may be exposed to alcohol for the first time, and are adjusting to life away from home in a culture where excessive alcohol consumption is widely accepted.

Reports from the CDC suggest that underage drinkers often consume more alcohol in a given session than older drinkers. What's more, binge drinking is rampant throughout this category, with estimates suggesting that 90% of alcohol consumed by individuals in the young adult subtype is through binge drinking. Binge drinking is defined as excessive alcohol consumption that results in a blood alcohol concentration (BAC) of up to or greater than 0.08g/dl. Typically, this occurs over two hours when a man consumes five alcoholic beverages, or when a woman has four, according to the NIAAA.

The NIAAA estimates that as many as 20% of college students experience some form of alcohol addiction during their time in school. Typically, the young adult subtype doesn't usually seek help for their alcoholism. This may be due to the fact that heavy drinking is widely considered an acceptable behavior during the college years, despite the fact that it can cause irreversible damage to the developing brains of young adults. It is generally assumed that young adults will grow out of their phase of heavy drinking, and many of them do. However, that does not mean that it isn't causing significant mental and physical damage during these years. What's more, not all individuals "grow out" of heavy drinking – and it should not be assumed that this will be the case.

Young Antisocial Subtype

Typically, young antisocial drinkers are in their 20s, and usually began abusing alcohol at a young age. In fact, it is the early abuse of alcohol that leads to the development of this subtype of alcoholism, due to the effects of binge and heavy drinking on the brain. Individuals who drink heavily at a young age (such as binge drinking on five days or more in a 4-week period), are more likely to develop alcoholism later in life. This is due to the effects that alcohol has on the chemistry of the brain, and the cravings and withdrawal symptoms that are experienced when these individuals do stop drinking.

Young individuals may be more susceptible to alcohol abuse due to the fact that young brains are still developing their prefrontal cortex. This region of the brain is responsible for impulse control and regulating emotions, meaning that young adults may be more likely to undertake risky behavior (such as excessive alcohol consumption) without considering or fearing the outcomes of this behavior. What's more, the National Institute on Drug Abuse (NIDA) reports that excessive drinking at a young age dramatically increases the likelihood of an individual suffering from addiction and substance abuse disorders later in life.

Having a family history of alcoholism is a strong risk factor for the young antisocial subtype, with around half of individuals falling into this category of alcoholism reporting alcoholism in their family. What's more, 50% of these individuals suffer from antisocial personality disorder, which dramatically increases the risk of developing alcoholism or substance abuse. In part, individuals in this category turn to alcohol in an attempt to reduce their social anxiety and inhibitions. Typically, alcohol increases self-confidence and lowers inhibitions, making it the perfect ice-breaker for individuals who often don't feel relaxed in social situations.

Functional Alcoholic Subtype

Individuals suffering from functional alcoholism are usually middle-aged, and often have a high level of education. These sufferers often seem very well-adjusted and "normal" to an outsider – they usually have a reliable job and income and a happy and loving family life. Generally, these people are often not what we think of as typical alcoholism sufferers, and they tend to do a good job of keeping their alcoholism to themselves. It is estimated that around 20% of all individuals suffering from alcoholism in the United States fall into the category of functional alcoholism. Often, these individuals are described as leading "double lives" and are able to compartmentalize their issues with alcohol so that they do not affect other aspects of their life.

Unlike other individuals with alcoholism, those in the functional alcoholism category can usually perform all the daily tasks that are required of them, such as holding down a stable job and showing up each day to work, and meeting family obligations.

What's more, people close to the individual, such as a spouse or relative, may make excuses for their drinking whenever any questions are raised.

Most individuals in the functional alcoholism subgroup are unlikely to seek professional help, justifying that they do not have a problem because they are still able to live their lives and meet their obligations and commitments. Often, many individuals are prompted to seek help for their alcohol abuse when they hit "rock bottom," or find themselves in an undesirable situation. Often, individuals in the functional alcoholism category never reach this point; thus, they are less likely to either realize they have a problem or decide to seek help for it.

It is estimated that around 50% of individuals in the functional alcoholism subtype smoke cigarettes, and around 30% have a family history of alcoholism. What's more, studies show that approximately 25%

of these individuals have had at least one instance of major depressive disorder throughout their lives, a condition that often goes hand in hand with alcoholism.

Intermediate Familial Subtype

It is estimated that just under 20% of individuals suffering from alcoholism in the United States fall into the intermediate familial category of alcoholism. Generally, these individuals are middle-aged, and around 50% of them have a family history of alcoholism. Interestingly, a majority of these individuals smoke cigarettes, possibly suggesting that people in this subgroup are more likely to develop addictions. Along similar lines, almost 20% experience marijuana or cocaine abuse at some stage of their lives. This is particularly dangerous, because the abuse of more than one substance compounds the side effects and risk factors, putting excess stress on many systems of the body.

It is estimated that around half of the individuals in the intermediate familial alcoholism subgroup either are currently experiencing clinical depression or have experienced this at some stage in their lives. Staggeringly, around 20% of these individuals also have bipolar disorder, which has been known to occur simultaneously with alcohol. This is in part because many individuals with bipolar (and other mental health conditions) use alcohol to self-medicate, and end up becoming dependent on the drug. The mood swings that are so common with bipolar disorder can be somewhat tempered by the effects of alcohol, but this is no substitute for prescription medication that is specifically designed to treat bipolar disorder.

For individuals suffering from co-occurring disorders, such as alcoholism and bipolar disorder, the most effective form of treatment is an integrated program. This facilitates the management of both disorders at the same time and offers treatment for each condition without affecting the other. In the intermediate familial alcoholism subcategory, around 25% of individuals seek medical treatment for alcohol-related issues.

Chronic Severe Subtype

Chronic severe alcoholism most closely resembles what people think of as typical alcoholism. This category consists of less than 10% of those individuals with alcoholism in the United States and is usually made up of middle-aged drinkers. Usually, these individuals began drinking heavily at a young age, and have struggled with alcohol addiction for decades. This causes significant mental and physical health issues, with a majority of individuals in this subgroup also suffering from an antisocial personality disorder. Often, these individuals let drinking rule their lives to the point where they are consistently making poor decisions, and can regularly end up on the wrong side of the law.

Those with severe chronic alcoholism suffer from psychiatric disorders (including bipolar disorder, depression, and various personality disorders) more commonly than any other subgroup. What's more, many violent crimes are committed due to alcohol abuse, and those with severe chronic alcoholism often experience increased levels of aggression. This can increase the likelihood of violent crimes, with around 40% of violent crimes committed in the United States, citing alcohol abuse as a contributing factor. Individuals in the chronic severe alcoholism subgroup will often do whatever it takes to obtain their next drink, which is another reason why crime can be so common among individuals with alcoholism in this group.

Almost 80% of individuals in this subcategory have some degree of family history of alcoholism, or a genetic predisposition to drug or alcohol abuse or addiction. These individuals are much more likely than the general population to abuse drugs such as opioids, cocaine, and marijuana. What's more, sufferers of severe chronic alcoholism are more likely to experience severe problems and hardships as a result of their drinking, such as homelessness, unemployment, unhealthy relationships, financial issues, and of course, additional health problems.

Although a majority of individuals suffering from alcoholism fit into the above categories (with some overlap), this is not an exhaustive list of the problems that alcohol abuse can cause. Alcohol affects each individual differently and can have marked effects on how we behave, the lifestyle choices we make, and how we interact with others.

How Does Alcohol Affect Our Behavior?

It's widely accepted that alcohol makes us act differently to how we normally would without the drug. Drinking alcohol can affect all kinds of human behaviors, including how we interact socially with others, our emotional responses to certain situations, and how we view ourselves and our lives. When we drink alcohol, we may feel more confident about how we look, we may feel happier about our lives, and we may like our friends more. However, alcohol doesn't instantly change our appearance, our lives, or our friends, so what is the reason for feeling so different from a couple of drinks in our system?

Ultimately, it's all because of the effects that alcohol has on the brain, and the way it tricks us into feeling great about ourselves without actually helping us to change or improve the aspects we don't like. For many years, the effects of alcohol on the brain were poorly understood, but decades of research and improvements in neural imaging technology such as functional magnetic resonance imaging (fMRI), PET (positron emission tomography) scans, and other functional brain imaging methods.

These research techniques can show scientists which

parts of the brain are active at different times, based on increased electrical activity and blood flow in those areas. This is highly useful in determining how the brain responds to certain stimuli. For example, scientists can perform imaging studies on an individual's brain while that individual is retelling a memory from their childhood. The parts of the brain that are responsible for storing and recalling long-term memories will be more active during this time and require more oxygen and blood flow. The increase in blood flow to these areas, as well as the increase in electrical activity as the relevant neurons, are firing electrical signals, helps show scientists which parts of the brain we use for memory.

The same experimental procedure can be used to determine which parts of the brain we use for catching a ball and writing a letter. What's more, these experimental techniques have proved very useful in enhancing our understanding of addiction pathways, and the immediate effects that alcohol consumption has on our brains. Scientists can see the changes that occur in the brain immediately after drinking, and also after several years of heavy drinking. They can use these techniques to study alcohol addiction, withdrawal, abstinence, and relapse, helping to paint a clearer picture of the many ways in which alcohol can affect brain activity, and in turn, our behaviors, actions, relationships, personalities, lifestyles, and so much more.

The Effects Of Alcohol On Risk-Taking Behaviors

Of course, there is still a lot we don't understand about the brain, and more specifically, how alcohol affects it. One thing we do know is that alcohol has a strong effect on the information processing pathways our brain normally uses to regulate and inhibit impulse responses. As a direct result of this, alcohol impairs our ability to foresee negative consequences to a given action (such as driving home when we've had too many drinks), making us more likely to take risks, and go ahead with activities that may be dangerous, or that we wouldn't normally do sober. By reducing the likelihood that our brain will say "no" to an idea we have, alcohol has great power over our actions and reactions.

Current research seems to indicate that it's not just the act of alcohol consumption that increases our likelihood to perform risky behaviors. It has been hypothesized that individuals who consume alcohol at a young age undergo such drastic changes in brain chemistry that they are more likely to take risks as adults, whether they are under the influence of alcohol or not. This is just one example of the many ways in which alcohol can have long-lasting, dramatic effects on our behavior and personality. In a fascinating study performed in rats, animals aged the equivalent of human teenagers were given 24-hour access to alcohol [28]. Once these rats reached adulthood, they were given the opportunity to take a low risk and receive a small treat or to take a high risk and receive a larger treat. Perhaps unsurprisingly, the rats that had been exposed to alcohol at "teenagers" were much more likely to take the high-risk option, suggesting that alcohol fundamentally rewired the brains of these animals.

To further investigate how this was occurring, the researchers examined the brain function of the rats in question. They found significant changes in dopamine levels, and possible changes to GABA receptors, suggesting that these animals were experiencing a higher than normal pleasure response for the risks they were taking. In humans, this study suggests that the younger you experience alcohol, the more problems you can have later in life with the drug, and with other behaviors. This could have drastic implications in adults when it comes to drug use, gambling, sexual activities, and other behaviors that can be considered high-risk.

How Alcohol Affects Our Emotions

There's no denying that as well as affecting our

decision making, alcohol can have a drastic effect on our emotional state. Alcohol may bring about feelings of happiness initially, but long-term use, or even the day after a night of heavy drinking, our emotions can be much more negative. Drinking affects the emotional state of different people in different ways, through mechanisms that are not yet fully understood. In a survey of over 1,000 individuals in the United States, the emotional effects of alcohol described were diverse – nostalgia, creative, sad, happy, anxious, excited. Some people cry some people laugh, and some people get dangerously angry. Sometimes, an individual may experience all of these emotions – the effects of alcohol on our emotional health can be strong and unpredictable.

A large part of the effects that alcohol has on our emotions is through the cerebellum. The cerebellum is responsible for, among other things, partially controlling our memory and emotions. When alcohol is consumed, the levels of serotonin, a neurotransmitter involved in emotional regulation, are increased. Additionally, alcohol stimulates the release of endorphins. The combination of serotonin and endorphins leads to increased feelings of relaxation and happiness following alcohol consumption, at least in the short term. However, the more frequently an individual consumes alcohol, the more vulnerable their brain becomes to the drug. Over time, their mood can become more volatile and unpredictable.

Although alcohol may lead to feelings of relaxation and happiness in the short term, it is a chemical depressant when abused in the long term. This means that alcohol consumption suppresses neural activity, dulling the senses. If you are feeling upset, stressed, or angry, it's possible that alcohol will suppress those feelings, at least temporarily. For individuals predisposed to mental health conditions such as depression or anxiety disorders, alcohol can worsen the symptoms of these conditions. In cases of long-term, heavy drinking, alcohol abuse may even lead to suicidal thoughts or tendencies. Our emotions are based on delicate balances of neurotransmitters, and when these ratios are disturbed, such as following alcohol consumption, our emotions can run haywire.

As well as the cerebellum, the limbic system plays a very important role in controlling our emotions. Limbic system function can be suppressed by alcohol consumption, which results in our brain losing the ability to control our emotions. This can cause us to act irrationally, and individuals under the influence of alcohol are often more outwardly emotional. This may manifest in terms of sadness, joy, anger, or a range of other emotions – alcohol doesn't determine how we feel, it just suppresses our ability to control our feelings.

To counteract the alcohol's ability to depress neural function, the brain releases stimulants and stress hormones. Once the alcohol is metabolized and no longer affecting the body, the stimulants and stress hormones are still present. This can result in feelings of anxiety, which often prompts individuals to start drinking again, and the vicious cycle continues.

Understanding Alcohol And Aggression

One of the emotions most commonly associated with alcohol abuse is anger and aggression. The link between alcohol consumption and aggression is well established, with alcohol playing a role in many aggressive crimes. While the neural relationship between alcohol and aggression is complicated, it is widely accepted that not all individuals who consume alcohol become aggressive. It may only be a small subset of the alcohol-consuming population, but the effects of their behavior can often be felt widely. Families and loved ones can often become the targets of alcohol-fueled outbursts, with little warning.

Individuals who are most likely to become aggressive

when under the influence of alcohol are often more easily irritable and have limited control over their anger when sober. Additionally, these individuals typically display less empathy towards others when sober. It also appears that gender plays a role – men are significantly more likely than women to become aggressive following alcohol consumption. Though it is not fully understood why some individuals are more likely to become aggressive than others, it is possible that the decision-making process discussed earlier plays a role. Some individuals naturally have less control over their emotions and behaviors and are more likely to participate in risk-taking behaviors, even without the influence of alcohol.

It is possible that these individuals with less emotional control are more likely to become aggressive following alcohol consumption. What's more, adolescents and young adults are the most likely to become aggressive following alcohol intake, possibly due to the fact that their brains are still developing. Research has shown that individuals who have a dependence on alcohol are even more likely to behave aggressively. Each time these individuals drink alcohol, their decision making is impaired due to the alcohol in their system. This increases the likelihood of irrational, impulsive, and aggressive behavior. Staggeringly, these individuals may also become more likely to act impulsively even when they are sober, lending further evidence to alcohol's ability to re-wire the brain and cause significant neurochemical changes.

In a study performed on rats, it was observed that a small subset of animals became aggressive when under the influence of alcohol, similar to the trend seen in humans. Further investigation revealed that these animals have lower levels of serotonin and higher levels of dopamine than their less-aggressive counterparts. Similar changes have been observed in adult humans who chronically abuse alcohol, and have also been implicated in aggressive behavior exhibited by binge drinkers who aren't addicted to alcohol [29]. What's more, individuals with lower serotonin levels are also more likely to consume excess quantities of alcohol.

Can Alcohol Really Change Our Personality?

People often comment that their whole personality changes following alcohol consumption, or that they see this happen to their friends when they are under the influence of alcohol. Alcohol can elicit some changes in our personalities, but these changes are usually relatively minor. One particular aspect of an individual's personality can be drastically altered by alcohol, and that is extroversion. This makes sense – many people find that they are more talkative when under the influence of alcohol, and perhaps say things that they wouldn't (or shouldn't) normally say. This is due to the dulling effect that alcohol has on the regulatory regions of the brain, enabling riskier behaviors.

Although alcohol can be blamed for a lot of things, it can't necessarily be blamed for changing your personality. When alcohol is consumed, it enhances the personality you already have – these traits already exist and are just heightened following alcohol intake. One theory suggests that alcohol disinhibits whatever underlying inhibitions that an individual already has. For example, someone that is generally happy may become happier under the influence of alcohol. However, somebody who is suppressing a lot of anger or resentment may not suppress these feelings as effectively following alcohol intake, leading to an outburst of aggression.

Many people try to use alcohol to dull their feelings, but in the end, those feelings are still there once the drug wears off. What's more, you may be opening yourself up to an explosion of unaddressed emotions due to the unpredictable nature of alcohol and its powerful effects on our feelings and emotions.

In short, alcohol can't completely change an individual's personality and turn them into someone new. However, it can amplify feelings we may already be experiencing, or trying to suppress, and may have noticeable effects on our personalities in both the short and long term. Alcohol affects everybody differently, and can even have different effects on the same person at different times. The effects of alcohol are largely unpredictable, and the drug can cause significant problems for an individual's social and emotional health.

How The Effects Of Alcohol Change Based On Your Gender

Much research has been performed into the differing effects alcohol has on men and women. Although the drug can affect everyone differently, it does appear that gender plays a large role in how alcohol affects an individual, and how likely an individual is to develop alcoholism. As well as gender, individuals of different ages can be affected very differently by alcoholism. Alcoholism in an adolescent usually manifests differently to that of a middle-aged individual. There are many biological and environmental reasons for these differences, some of which have been well established. Let's take a look at how alcohol and alcoholism can have different effects on men, women, and adolescents.

Alcoholism In Men

Overall, men seem to tolerate alcohol much better than women. Men can drink more alcohol, metabolize the drug faster, and become less impaired by alcohol. This is reflected in the safe alcohol intake guidelines of most countries – "safe" levels of alcohol intake are always higher for males than they are for females. In part, men are less affected by alcohol because they are generally larger than women, have a higher water content, and also typically have higher levels of the enzyme alcohol dehydrogenase, which is found in the liver and is responsible to converting alcohol to bi-products and removing it from the bloodstream.

It also appears that male bodies can tolerate alcohol abuse better in the long term than women. Chronic alcohol abuse in men does not result in death as frequently as it does in women, and alcohol-related health problems are lower in males with alcoholism than in females. Males with alcoholism are also less likely to suffer an alcohol-related injury than their female counterparts. When it comes to sexual health, men suffering from alcoholism can find it difficult to maintain an erection, may experience reduced sexual desire, and are more likely to have fertility problems. Males with alcoholism may also experience increased sexual aggression.

Despite tolerating and metabolizing the drug better, men are more prone to developing alcoholism than women. Research indicates that men are four times more likely than women to drink heavily, and twice as likely to develop alcoholism. What's more, males suffering from alcoholism are more likely to engage in risk-taking behaviors than their female counterparts, which increases their risk of injury or death. Men with alcoholism generally have higher rates of alcohol-related injuries than women.

It has long been suggested that one of the reasons why men are more likely to suffer from alcoholism is due to the short-term effects that alcohol has on mood enhancement and stress relief. Historically, men have been more likely to suffer from day-to-day stress than women, due to being the primary source of income in a household and working to support a family. Working men would turn to alcohol to improve their mood after a long day at work or reduce their stress levels. Although family and workplace dynamics have dramatically changed in the last half-century, it's possible that these changes are yet to be reflected in scientific experiments.

As well as the effects of societal standards, there may

be neurological explanations as to why men are more likely to succumb to alcoholism than women. In general, women tend to have lower dopamine levels than men, and higher levels of the D2 dopamine receptor than men. This receptor has been shown to play a role in the development of addiction, as well as alcoholic complications [30]. The differences in the dopamine system between men and women could help to explain why men are more likely to suffer from alcohol addiction, as dopamine is heavily implicated in reward and addiction pathways, as previously discussed.

Although the physical differences between males and females with alcoholism are pronounced, it may be the behavioral differences that are more noticeable. Male alcoholism is often characterized by increased feelings and expression of aggression [31], which is not seen as frequently in women suffering from alcoholism. The reasons for this difference are unclear but may come back to social learning and what is considered socially acceptable behaviors.

Typically, aggressive behavior is more socially acceptable in men than in women [32], which would simply mean that males feel more comfortable expressing their aggression as they have been allowed to do so their whole life.

Alternatively, the difference in aggression levels between men and women with alcoholism may reflect a difference in the degree to which alcohol alters the mechanisms of behavioral control between the two genders. It is possible that alcohol's ability to disinhibit behaviors that are normally inhibited, such as aggression or risk-taking actions, is heightened in men. Indeed, studies have shown that alcohol reduces the inhibitory effects on male impulse control more than it does on female impulse control. This implies that men are more likely to act spontaneously and impulsively following alcohol consumption than women are, with little regard for the consequences of their actions.

Because men and women respond differently to alcohol, treatments for alcoholism generally differ between the two genders. Effective alcoholism treatments need to take into consideration hormone levels and neurotransmitter systems in order to provide effective treatment. Of course, a wide range of behavioral and social factors also must be considered when treating male versus female patients suffering from alcoholism. By better understanding the differences in how alcohol addiction manifests between men and women, treatments can be more effectively tailored to provide the best results.

Alcoholism In Women

Many of the first scientific studies assessing the causes, effects, and treatments of alcoholism were performed using only male subjects. It has only been in later years that alcoholism in women has become a more heavily researched field. The findings coming out of these studies suggest that alcoholism manifests very differently in female subjects. Alcohol intake affects women in different ways to men, and long-term alcohol abuse has distinct (and often more severe) effects on the female body. There are many ways in which alcoholism manifests differently in women compared to men, in terms of behavior, neurochemical changes, and physical side effects.

Although men have a greater propensity towards developing alcoholism, women suffer the most when it comes to alcoholism-associated bodily damage. Following binge drinking or chronic alcohol abuse, women are more likely to suffer brain damage or other organ damage. Women typically have lower levels of the enzyme alcohol dehydrogenase [33], which is crucial to the metabolism of alcohol in the liver. In fact, men have around 50% more alcohol dehydrogenase than women. Reduced levels of this enzyme mean that alcohol is not removed from the bloodstream as quickly as it is for men, which means the toxic effects of the drug have more time to act on various body systems. What's more, women are typically smaller, meaning that a lower dose of alcohol circulates through the body at a higher concentration.

The reduced rate of alcohol metabolism in women means that women have higher blood alcohol levels than me after consuming the same amount of alcohol. This means that women become intoxicated faster, and can experience the potentially deadly effects of alcohol poisoning at a lower dose than their male counterparts. Although women are less likely than men to succumb to alcoholism, they are more likely to experience detrimental and significant health challenges as a result of long-term alcohol abuse.

Another difference in the effects of alcoholism on men and women is due to hormonal differences. The levels of various hormones circulating in the bloodstream of female bodies fluctuate with the different phases of the menstrual cycle. Women can experience increased and prolonged intoxication at certain phases of the cycle, meaning that alcohol can affect their bodies in unpredictable ways [34]. Oral contraceptives have the same effect, as they alter hormone levels. Women taking oral contraceptives experienced a slowing of the rate at which alcohol is eliminated from the body, and as a result, can be more strongly affected by alcohol. Typically, females taking oral contraceptives experience the sedating effects of alcohol for longer than those who are not. Excessive alcohol consumption can also result in disruption of the menstrual cycle and increase the chances of infertility [35].

Unfortunately, women are more likely than men to suffer from the many debilitating health effects that come with long-term alcohol abuse. Females with alcoholism have a higher risk of liver disease and cirrhosis than men, as well as other alcohol-related liver diseases. What's more, women who drink excessively are at increased risk of heart damage and numerous cancers, including cancers of the breast, mouth, throat, esophagus, liver, and colon compared to men [36]. Women are at greater risk for all types of alcohol-related health concerns than men due to the drug circulating in their bloodstream for longer after each beverage is consumed. The toxic effects of alcoholism are felt throughout the body, on every cell in every organ.

For some women, alcoholism doesn't just affect their own bodies. Alcohol consumption during pregnancy can have serious effects on the health of the fetus and mother-to-be alike. Women who consume alcohol during pregnancy significantly increase the chances of giving birth to a baby with fetal alcohol spectrum disorders (FASD) [37]. This spectrum of conditions includes a wide range of physical problems, as well as issues with learning and behavior. Typically, an individual affected with FASD experiences a mixture of physical and psychological symptoms.

A fetus receives its nutrients from its mother through

the umbilical cord. Anything that is in the mother's bloodstream passes through the cord into the fetus' blood. Unfortunately, alcohol can also enter the bloodstream of a fetus through the umbilical cord. There is no safe time or amount of alcohol to consume during pregnancy. Alcohol can cause problems for the developing fetus from before a woman even knows she is pregnant until the end of the third trimester. Even beverages with relatively low alcoholic content, such as beer or wine, are harmful to a fetus.

FASDs can range from mild to severe and can affect different individuals in different ways. Physical symptoms may include abnormal facial features, including a smooth ridge between the upper lip and the nose. Individuals with an FASD may also be shorter than average, with a small head circumference, low body weight, and a lack of physical coordination. Psychological symptoms include hyperactive behavior, a short attention span, poor memory, learning disabilities, and difficulty in school. Sufferers may also experience delays in their speech and language, a low IQ or intellectual disability, poor judgment skills, and vision or hearing problems. As infants, FASD sufferers have feeding and sleeping problems and can develop heart, kidney, or bone defects.

Fetal Alcohol Syndrome (FAS) is the most severe of FASDs and can result in death [38]. The alcohol-related neurodevelopmental disorder is another condition caused by drinking during pregnancy and is characterized by intellectual disabilities, learning difficulties, and poor impulse control. There is no cure for FASDs, though studies have shown that behavioral treatment at a young age can help to improve a child's development.

Alcohol abuse in women also increases their risk of violent victimization. In a survey of female college students, a direct and significant relationship was found between the amount of alcohol consumed and the number of unwanted sexual experiences they reported. In another study, female high school students who reported alcohol use over the previous 12-month period were more likely to experience abuse from their partner in the form of shoving, kicking, or punching.

Women don't tolerate alcohol as well as men. They feel the effects faster, and they are more likely to experience negative long-term health effects such as liver failure or cancer. What's more, although women are less likely to develop alcoholism than their male counterparts, they are more likely to suffer abuse at the hands of it.

Alcoholism In Adolescents

There is never a good time to drink alcohol in excess, but alcohol abuse during adolescence is particularly damaging. With so much brain development occurring well into our twenties, this is a time when neural pathways are particularly susceptible to the effects of alcoholism.

Unfortunately, this critical period of brain development also coincides with a time in the lives of young people where they are most likely to experiment with alcohol and consume excessive amounts of the drug. Social pressures, hormones, and environmental factors all play a role in adolescent drinking and alcoholism, with binge drinking being a particularly prevalent act among adolescents. Surveys of adolescents suggest that between 30% and 40% of 12th grade male students report binge drinking, with around 25% of female students reporting the same. Research also indicates that the gender gap is closing in this statistic – each year, more and more female students report binge drinking and alcohol abuse.

Studies have shown that there is a strong link between heavy drinking during adolescence and alcohol abuse later in life [39]. Teens and young adults who start drinking at a young age are much more likely to have an unhealthy relationship with alcohol and become dependent on the drug as their lives progress. This could be due to the strong effects that alcohol has on the developing brain – these individuals are almost "brainwashed" into feeling as though they need alcohol later in life. Alternatively, alcohol abuse during the adolescent years may be acting as a marker for alcohol abuse later in life, rather than a cause or a pre-cursor. It is possible that these individuals are already predisposed to alcohol (or other drugs) abuse or risk-taking behavior, and therefore more likely to develop alcoholism, regardless of their age.

For many young adults, adolescence is a time of their lives that can be very stressful. Leaving home, perhaps pursuing a college degree, and beginning life in the workforce are all stressful experiences, and taking your first steps into adulthood is never easy. Combined with debt, relationships, hormones, and a time of extreme change, many individuals find that they need a little help in dealing with all of this. In many cases, alcohol becomes a coping mechanism, and the brain loses its natural abilities to handle stress and other negative feelings, instead of relying on the effects of alcohol. This leads to a negative feedback look where more and more alcohol is required, and eventually, alcoholism develops.

The anxiety and stress that comes with entering adulthood is a major factor in why many young adults turn to alcohol. In a survey conducted in the 1990s, it was determined that stress is a clear influencer of alcohol consumption in adolescents, but not a clear influencer in adults. In fact, the level of stress that an adolescent felt was the second most powerful predictor of whether or not they would consume alcohol. Unsurprisingly, the most powerful predictor of this was whether or not their peers were consuming alcohol.

The importance of the critical phase of brain development that occurs during adolescence cannot be overstated. By the time we reach adolescence, our brain has a fairly good idea of what can be considered "important" information, and what is "irrelevant." For neurons that are used more frequently, i.e., those considered to be important, the brain forms additional connections around these cells, strengthening their signals. On the other hand, existing connections between neurons that aren't used as often or aren't considered "critical" by the brain are often pruned away, allowing the brain to focus more on the regions it uses more often. This can be compared to our muscles – if you are a runner, your body strengthens your leg muscles because they are more critical and relevant to your needs. Essentially, the same thing is happening in the brain of young adults.

The extensive re-wiring of the brain that happens during this time may help to explain why alcohol abuse during adolescence is associated with memory problems and other neuropsychological deficits. In particular, the dopaminergic system of the brain undergoes numerous changes during adolescence. This can have profound effects on adolescent behavior and brain function and represents a time during which young adults are vulnerable to the effects of alcohol or other drugs [40]. Adjustments to neural connections in the prefrontal cortex also occur during adolescence – an area of the brain implicated in memory, spatial learning, and emotional processing. The levels of various neurotransmitters are in flux during this time, altering stress responses, memory processing, and the regulation of emotions. Exposing an already-vulnerable adult brain to excessive alcohol can lead to permanent, detrimental neurological changes.

Alcohol abuse during adolescence can have profound effects on the hippocampus – a region of the brain implicated in learning and memory. Research has shown that adolescents with alcoholism have a significantly smaller hippocampus than those who do not drink. What's more, adolescents who started drinking at an older age had a larger hippocampus than those who were drinking from a younger age. This suggests that during this critical phase of neural development, every day counts when it comes to alcohol consumption.

In terms of characteristic behaviors resulting from alcoholism, adolescents do tend to display different traits when compared to adults with alcoholism. The most noticeable behavior is an increase in risk-taking behaviors among adolescents when under the influence of alcohol. Even without alcohol, adolescents are more likely to participate in risky behaviors than older adults. Under the influence, adolescents are more likely to do things such as to get behind the wheel of a car or participate in high-risk sexual activities. Indeed, a vast number of deaths in adolescents associated with alcohol are related to high-risk behaviors, like motor vehicle incidents or other preventable accidents.

Young bodies, and in particular young brains, are extremely vulnerable to the effects of alcohol. Consuming alcohol during adolescence coincides with a time when the central nervous system is undergoing so many changes and is in the middle of a critical phase of development. Although there is never a safe time to consume alcohol, heavy drinking during adolescence is one of the worst and can have long-term severe neuro-psychological consequences.

5. The Keys To Recognizing An Alcohol Addiction

Recognizing an alcohol addiction, whether it be in yourself or somebody around you, can be very difficult to do. For many of us, we may know deep down that we drink too much, too frequently, and that our craving for a glass of wine after a busy day at work isn't healthy. But how much alcohol is too much? Where is the line between "enjoying a drink or two" and "developing alcoholism," and how do you know if you've crossed it? We all say we could stop drinking whenever we wanted, but could we, really? Given that we know how damaging alcohol is for our bodies and minds, why haven't we?

If you find yourself asking these questions, it may be time to reassess your relationship with alcohol. In this chapter, we will explore how to recognize unhealthy drinking habits in yourself and how to know when treatment is necessary. We will also discuss how to recognize alcoholism in someone around you, and how you can provide them with the help they may desperately need.

How Much Is Too Much?

When it comes to alcohol, there is so much contradicting information about "safe levels" of consumption. In essence, no amount of alcohol is safe, as even one alcoholic beverage can cause damage to your mind and body. That said, there are guidelines in place that can be followed to ensure you are not consuming an amount of alcohol that will cause liver damage or lead to severe damage to other organs.

So, how much alcohol is an acceptable amount? The CDC currently recommends that alcohol be consumed in moderation, which they define as up to one alcoholic drink per day for women, and up to two alcoholic drinks per day for men. Over a week, these guidelines extend to up to 11 drinks for women or 17 drinks for men. When interpreting these guidelines, it is important to understand that one drink is not a pint of beer or a glass of wine – make sure you understand the serving sizes before following these guidelines. One drink is defined as one 12-oz beer (whereas a pint is 16oz), one 5-oz glass of wine (measure this – you may be surprised how much more you've been pouring yourself), or a 1.5-oz shot of distilled spirits or liquor. The one-to-two drinks per day rule do not mean that you can skip alcohol for five days and then consume eight drinks in one night, as binge drinking is far worse for your health than drinking in moderation.

Many people exceed the recommended alcohol intake from time to time. Having three drinks on a special occasion isn't going to have a serious effect on your health, but doing it regularly may. By reducing your alcohol consumption to a safe level, you will have more energy, sleep better, reduce your risk of numerous health conditions, and, most importantly – feel as though you are in charge of your drinking.

The CDC guidelines don't suggest that you should consume one alcoholic beverage every day, just that you should not consume more than once per day. It is very important to take regular breaks from drinking alcohol. Make sure you have at least two nights a week where you don't consume alcohol, to ensure that your brain doesn't develop a dependency on the drug, or become used to constant stimulation from alcohol. If you are concerned about your relationship with alcohol, you may want to take a break for longer – consider having an alcohol-free weekend, or even a whole week, just to ensure you can do it. You might be surprised by how healthy and happy you feel at the end of a week of sobriety.

Recognizing Alcohol Addiction In Yourself

It can be surprisingly difficult to recognize an alcohol addiction in yourself. This is why so many people rely on their loved ones to provide them with the support they need to come to terms with their problem and seek help for their drinking. Without even realizing, you may have tricked yourself into thinking that your alcohol consumption is normal, or justified, or that it's just happening because you're busy or stressed at work. If someone tries to talk with you about your alcohol consumption, make sure you listen to them, and don't dismiss their concerns – they may be able to see things more clearly than you can.

If you're worried you may be suffering from alcoholism, use these warning signs to help determine whether or not you have a problem with excessive alcohol consumption. Remember, not all of these traits have to hit home – you may be suffering from alcoholism even if you only experience some of the warning signs described below.

Have You Experienced Temporary Blackouts Or Short-Term Memory Loss?

Memory loss or blacking out from drinking is a red flag for excessive alcohol consumption. It can indicate that you are not in control of your drinking, or that you don't realize how much alcohol you are consuming. If this happens to you on a semi-regular basis (such as once every two months or more), it means you are consuming far too much alcohol, far too frequently. Drinking uncontrollably like this is often a sign of alcoholism, and you should take immediate action.

Regularly drinking to the point of blacking out is not just bad for your liver, it can also put you in very dangerous situations. When you are this drunk, it can be easy for others to take advantage of you, or difficult to safely make your way home. Drinking to the point of blacking out means you are no longer in control of your actions, and not being able to retrace your movements or recall your behavior the next day can further complicate your life. Drinking this heavily puts great strain on your relationships, as well as your physical and emotional wellbeing.

Ask Yourself Why You Drink

Sometimes, our motives for drinking can tell us just as much about our relationship with alcohol as the quantity of alcohol we consume can. If you reflexively pour yourself a drink after you get home from work, you may be drinking more out of a dependency than for enjoyment. If you usually only drink alcohol when you are out with friends, you are more likely to be a social drinker who has a healthy relationship with alcohol – there's nothing wrong with unwinding at a happy hour every now and again with your social circle.

When it comes to alcoholism, most people are drinking to help them relax or feel better. Almost every individual with a drug or alcohol addiction cites emotional reasons as the cause – from stress to depression or anxiety and everything in between. Drinking to self-medicate or help you feel better is a very dangerous and slippery slope. It doesn't actually help you deal with the problems you may be experiencing, and the longer you try to do this for, the more alcohol you will need to boost your mood. Drinking for emotional reasons is a common sign of alcoholism, and suggests you should re-evaluate your relationship with alcohol.

How Familiar Are You With Hangovers?

Let's be honest, pretty much everyone knows how a hangover feels. It's easy to over-indulge occasionally by accident, and one or two hangovers in your lifetime aren't going to cut years off your life. However, it is important to remember that a hangover is essentially your body's response to being poisoned. It is an indication that you have caused damage to your organs, that you are extremely dehydrated, and that you have consumed more alcohol than your liver can comfortably process. If hangovers are a regular part of your life, you are drinking far too much. If you're used to waking up on a Sunday feeling terrible, or if you regularly have headaches at work as a result of being hungover, this is a clear warning sign of alcoholism, and you should consider taking further action.

Does Alcohol Affect Your Day-To-Day Life?

One of the characteristic signs of alcoholism is seen when alcohol interferes with an individual's day-to-day life. If you are drinking before work, or before you need to drive somewhere, and as a result of this are shirking your responsibilities, your relationship with alcohol is clearly unhealthy. If you are experiencing problems at school or work, such as keeping up with your workload, or missing days due to hangovers, alcohol has become an unhealthy part of your life. Similarly, if alcohol is affecting your relationship with your friends, family, or significant other, you may be prioritizing alcohol over these people, which indicates an unhealthy prioritization of alcohol. Many people suffering from addictions turn away from their friends and families, particularly if these people try to start a conversation around alcohol consumption and seeking help.

Are You Comfortable Talking About Your Alcohol Intake?

To expand on the last point, many individuals suffering from addiction are not comfortable talking about their alcohol or drug use. Typically, denial is a common sign of alcohol addiction – you may lie about your alcohol consumption to your friends, family, or even medical professionals. If you find yourself hiding your drinking, such as drinking secretively or going to a bar alone after work, it can be a sign of a much bigger problem.

If the people around you have tried to talk to you about your drinking, and you have dismissed their concerns or even tried to distance yourself from these people, this may indicate that you know deep down that their concern is justified. Often, individuals with alcoholism aren't ready to talk about their problems and instead turn away from those who are trying to offer help. If you are lying about your drinking or shutting the people out who are trying to help you, it will be much more difficult to find the help you need to break the cycle of alcoholism. As well as lying to others about your alcohol consumption, lying to yourself, or making excuses for your drinking is common in individuals suffering from alcoholism.

How To Recognize Alcoholism In Somebody Else

Many people who drink heavily or have an unhealthy relationship with alcohol are actually quite good at hiding their drinking from those around them. Even some individuals suffering from chronic alcoholism can hold down a steady job and maintain relationships while alcohol controls their lives. Just because these people appear to have things under control, it does not mean that their problem with alcohol should not be addressed. Not only is it causing long-term, permanent damage to their physical and emotional health, but heavy drinking may also be an indication of a deeper problem. Alcohol may be used to cope with mental illness, stress, chronic pain, or a range of physical or emotional issues. Until the alcoholism is treated, these underlying problems cannot be dealt with. If you notice any of the following traits or behaviors in someone you are close to, they may be suffering from alcoholism and need help in seeking the treatment they clearly need.

Social Withdrawal Or Disinterest

If you are noticing that a friend or loved one doesn't seem as social as they once were, or that they are turning down invitations to spend time with you, alcoholism may be the cause. Of course, there can be many reasons for social withdrawal – perhaps they are just busy, or perhaps they are dealing with a mental health problem such as depression. However, if no other obvious cause presents itself, alcohol may be the reason. Alcoholism often results in social withdrawal, as individuals struggling with addiction would typically spend their time drinking alone rather than in the company of others.

Similarly, if you suspect that someone close to you is suffering from alcoholism, you may notice that they don't seem to be finding as much enjoyment in day-to-day activities as they once were. They may have given up on hobbies they once enjoyed, or they may have quit their gym or sports club. Often, alcoholism causes individuals to turn their backs on their social lives and hobbies. Even if alcohol is not the cause, social withdrawal or disinterest may indicate another problem, such as a mental health issue like depression, that your loved one may need help for, or wish to talk about.

Regularly Under The Influence Of Alcohol

Another telltale warning sign of alcoholism is catching up with a friend who is drinking every time you see them. It may sound obvious, but it can actually be difficult to realize that someone close to you is constantly intoxicated. If you have friends or family members that you only see in social settings, you may not even think twice about the fact that they always have a drink in their hand. However, you may notice subtle differences in their drinking habits compared to those of others around you. Typically, someone suffering from alcoholism will always be consuming alcohol. They will be the first person to order a drink, and the last person to leave the bar on a Friday night. There are also other subtle changes you can look for that signify unhealthy drinking.

If someone you know is suffering from alcoholism, you may notice that they always have to be drinking. They will order another drink usually before they finish the one they already have, and they will typically consume alcohol at a faster rate than others in your group. Even though they're drinking faster, they may not display signs of inebriation as quickly, due to the fact that their bodies are used to frequent, heavy alcohol consumption. You may also notice that they appear more relaxed after a few drinks – many individuals affected by alcoholism are quite anxious and seem preoccupied while they are sober.

If you recognize any of these signs in either yourself or someone else, it may be time to take action. It is important to note that not all of the above signs of alcoholism will be seen in a single individual – but even just one or two signs can indicate problem drinking. Rather than waiting for more signs to develop, it is best to intervene early. Early intervention often has more chance of success, as the addiction has not yet fully taken hold. In addition, intervening early can help to prevent permanent health damage, and can ensure that relationships with others are preserved rather than destroyed.

6. The Most Effective Ways To Treat Alcoholism

Whether for yourself or somebody else, seeking treatment for alcoholism is never an easy thing to do. The good news is that the first part – talking to someone about your or their struggles with alcohol and making the decision to seek treatment – is often the most difficult step in the path to recovery. Stay strong, surround yourself with loved ones, and know that better times lie ahead. It's never too late to seek help, but there is no better time than the present. Treating alcoholism is never an easy process, but following the steps and advice in this chapter gives you (or a loved one) the best possible chance of overcoming the burden of alcohol addiction.

The Importance Of Changing How You View Alcoholism

For too long, addictions (and in fact, a majority of mental health problems) have been viewed as weaknesses. Traditionally, it is thought that those people who turn to drugs or alcohol as taking the easy way out rather than facing their problems head-on. Now that we have a much better understanding of mental health and of how drugs and alcohol can affect our brains, we know that this is not the case. Addiction, and other mental health problems such as anxiety disorders and depression, are real diseases, just like cancer or diabetes. Nobody chooses to suffer from these conditions, and just like cancer or diabetes, treatment is required for mental health disorders in order to return to health.

If you, or someone you know, are suffering from alcohol addiction, it is important not to feel ashamed or embarrassed. A majority of educated individuals now realize that these are very real diseases that need treating – not a sign of weakness. If you are dealing with alcoholism yourself, don't let anyone try to tell you that you are weak, or that you need to simply "snap out of it." Likewise, if you are helping someone else through their struggles with alcoholism, make sure you help to make them realize that they have a disease that can be cured.

Talking openly about addiction and the importance of mental health is a crucial part of overcoming the stigma associated with these conditions. For so many people, the stigma that is unfortunately still associated with alcoholism plays a large role in why they don't want to seek help. Until their mindset is changed, and they understand that they have an illness that needs treatment, their struggles will continue. Breaking down barriers and talking openly about addiction, drug use, and the importance of understanding mental health can greatly improve how likely someone is to seek treatment.

What To Do When Someone Brings Up Your Drinking

Being confronted about your drinking can be embarrassing, scary, and often unexpected. It can lead to a lot of sudden emotions, with everything from anger and betrayal to embarrassment and shame. You may feel as though your best friends and family have been conspiring against you, which can make you feel betrayed or less likely to take their advice. Instead, it is important to remember that they are doing this out of love, and you should make an effort to hear them out, even if you may not understand why they think your drinking needs addressing.

Make sure you keep an open mind and listen to what they have to say. Keep your emotions in check – do not raise your voice, don't cut them off, and try to refrain from explaining yourself or making excuses. Remember that they love and care about you enough to do this and that they are only trying to help. Try not to feel isolated or outnumbered – everyone is on the same side. If things get too much and you need a bit of a break, just let them know. It can be a lot to deal with, and this will give you a chance to leave the room, catch your breath, and start to digest the information that is being directed at you. It is important not to walk out or give up on the intervention – your loved ones will likely just try again at a later date. You owe it to them to hear their concerns.

If you aren't too overwhelmed, try to use this opportunity to ask any questions you may have. Make sure you are clear as to why they feel as though you have a problem with drinking. They should explain this to you, but it is important that you fully understand the reasons behind their concern. You may also want to ask if anyone present has struggled with addiction in the past – it's possible that someone close to you has had a similar battle on their hands, and may have suggested or encouraged the intervention. This person can be a great help to you – they will have knowledge and advice that can really help you through this tough time.

Although you may be feeling embarrassed or

defensive, try to be open to their advice and suggestions. You can even ask people what they think you should do, and it's possible that some of them have even been expecting you to ask, and may have spoken to a doctor on your behalf or looked into rehabilitation options or facilities for you. Although this may seem like an invasion of privacy, it's actually a loving, caring gesture from the people closest to you who just want to see you return to health. Asking questions also shows that you are engaged, willing to listen and learn, and taking the situation seriously.

How To Stage An Effective Intervention

If the coin is flipped and you are worried about a loved one and their relationship with alcohol, it may be necessary to stage an intervention of your own. Before staging an intervention with multiple individuals from the person in question's life, you may wish to try just talking to them informally, one-on-one first. This can be a low-key way to bring up their drinking without creating an overwhelming or intense situation, and they may be receptive to your concerns and willing to seek help. Even if it doesn't work right away, it may open their minds to the fact that they could have a drinking problem, meaning that the intervention won't come as such a shock. If talking to the person one-on-one doesn't achieve anything, you may need to organize an intervention. It may seem like overkill, but an intervention is a highly effective way to get through to a loved one and help them to accept that they have a problem. It could even be a life-saving gesture, which is something worth remembering when you're debating whether or not to stage one.

Who Should Be Included In The Process?

Of course, it can be very difficult to know what to say during an intervention, and many people are afraid of the confrontation that can result from these types of discussions. If you approach other people close to the affected individual, make sure they are comfortable being involved in the intervention process. If not, they can always write a letter to the affected individual, detailing how they have been affected by this person's drinking habits. You can present these letters to the individual during the intervention.

In terms of who should be involved in the intervention process, it varies from person to person. Try to think of people who are close to the individual and have been affected by their drinking. Contact parents, siblings, spouses or partners, co-workers, and close friends, and also ask these people if they feel there is anyone else who should be included. If the individual has children, you may wish to include them, but only if you think they are able to handle what can potentially be a very intense confrontation. Try to think of people that the individual respects and will listen to, as these people offer the best chance of convincing the individual they need to seek help for their drinking.

Although you can stage an intervention alone, enlisting the help of an intervention specialist may make things easier, and increase the chances of a positive intervention. An intervention specialist will help you and the others intervening to create an intervention strategy. For each case, this will be slightly different, and the intervention specialist can help you to address the specific needs of your loved one. Their expertise will prove invaluable, and their presence at the intervention is more likely to keep things as civil and as productive as possible.

Practice Is Key

If you do utilize an intervention specialist, they will be able to educate you and the others intervening in alcohol addiction, what to expect from the intervention, and how your loved one will be feeling. In addition, they can also explain addiction recovery and rehabilitation so that you have an understanding of the paths and processes that lie ahead. Having this knowledge and showing that you care enough to research the subject will go a long way in helping to convince your loved one that you are doing this out of a place of love. The more they believe you care about them, the more your message is likely to hit home.

Make sure you and your intervention team take the time to rehearse and prepare for the intervention, preferably with the intervention specialist. Think about the ways that this individual's alcohol addiction has negatively impacted your life or hurt you. An individual struggling with alcohol addiction will often be blind as to how their actions negatively impact others – they're not really thinking of others at all. Your stories and speeches can help trigger a moment of clarity where the affected individual can see that there is more to life than alcohol. Read your stories as a group first – this will prepare each of you for the emotional aspect of the intervention, and also allow you to provide feedback to each other.

When preparing to schedule the intervention, make sure that you choose a time when the individual is most likely to be sober, and a location that is non-threatening and familiar. This will help everyone to feel more relaxed and will increase the chances of a positive outcome. There's no knowing how long the intervention will last, but typically a 30 to 90-minute timeframe is common. Although intervention specialists are professionals when it comes to de-escalating situations, it is impossible to control or predict how your loved one will react to the intervention. All you can do is try to keep the intervention as peaceful and productive as possible and remind the individual that you are all doing this because you love and care about them.

What To Expect After An Intervention

During the intervention, make sure you outline a plan for the individual regarding their rehabilitation and steps towards sobriety. Depending on the severity of their alcoholism, you may need to insist that they check in to a rehabilitation facility immediately. However, if you think there is a chance that they can take steps towards sobriety on their own (with your help, of course), it is always recommended to give them this option. You will need to set some rules and goals with the individual and be very firm with them when it comes to what you expect from them. Before the intervention ends, make sure you have arranged another time to meet in around seven days, to check in on their progress.

The recovery goals that you set for the individual will depend on their current drinking habits. If they are drinking very heavily, start by suggesting that they cut back rather than give up alcohol immediately. This can lead to a whole host of negative side-effects, and often leads to relapse. Slowly reducing alcohol intake is a much safer, and generally more effective method of beating alcoholism. It is recommended that you discuss different options with a medical professional, as they will have different recommendations based on how much alcohol the individual is currently consuming. They will be able to help your loved one beat alcoholism and regain control of their life in the safest way possible.

When you are setting recovery goals, make sure that you are very firm about the consequences if they are not met. For example, suggest that the affected individual must remain sober for three days until you meet again. Make sure they realize that there will be negative consequences if they are unable to stick to these goals. Choose relevant and severe consequences that will act as a real deterrent, such as removing children from their custody, or not allowing them to drive. Your intervention specialist may be able to help you come up with some relevant goals to set that will help motivate your loved one to beat their alcohol addiction and regain control of their life, once and for all.

Conclusion

According to the 2014 Global Drug Survey, alcohol is the world's most popular recreational drug. In the United States alone, more than 15 million individuals struggle with an alcohol use disorder, but less than 8% seek or receive treatment. Alcohol causes an enormous global health burden, but the trillion-dollar alcoholic beverage industry doesn't see it that way. Despite the fact that alcohol consumption is so dangerous and damaging to our health, its popularity only increases across the globe each year. New alcoholic beverages are created to target specific markets, such as gluten-free beers, sustainable wines, low-calorie options, and sweet and fruity mixed drinks to target younger drinkers. Alcohol is an epidemic, and it's not going anywhere.

The health effects of alcohol use and abuse have been well documented. Short-term effects of alcohol intake include decreased anxiety and increased relaxation, impaired motor skill function, loss of inhibitions, and an increased predisposition to risk-taking behaviors. This can be very dangerous – we may feel as though we're fine to drive home when we're really not, or put ourselves in other dangerous situations. In addition, high doses of alcohol can cause much more severe short-term problems, such as memory loss or "blacking out," unconsciousness, or even death.

The long-term effects of alcohol consumption are equally severe. Long-term alcohol intake is damaging for our digestive system, can cause kidney and liver failure, and increases our chances of developing heart diseases as well as a wide range of cancers. What's more, alcohol is highly addictive, and long-term use results in significant brain changes. Alcohol alters the levels of different neurotransmitters in the brain, which can have widespread effects on our memory, emotions, and rewards processing pathways. Alcohol addiction is very dangerous – it can cause severe physical and mental health damage, affect us financially, and destroy our relationships with the people closest to us.

Once the alcohol starts to impact your life and alter your brain circuitry, it can be very difficult to remove yourself from the vicious cycle of alcoholism. You may find yourself going from drinking a glass of wine after work to relax, drinking a whole bottle, to needing to drink every day just to get the same enjoyment from alcohol, and to feel relaxed. This can happen very quickly before you even realize how much you are coming to depend on alcohol. By this stage, alcohol has taken control of your life, and it is no easy feat to remove yourself from the grips of the drug.

Luckily, overcoming alcohol addiction is possible. It can take a lot of work, but with the help and support of close family and friends, you or a loved one suffering from alcoholism will be able to get back on your feet. Although it may be challenging, overcoming alcohol addiction and regaining control of your life is always worth it, no matter how difficult it may seem.

References

[1] Litovitz, T. (1986). The alcohols: ethanol, methanol, isopropanol, ethylene glycol. Pediatric Clinics of North America, 33(2), 311-323.

[2] Dengerink, H. A., & Fagan, N. J. (1978). Effect of alcohol on emotional responses to stress. Journal of Studies on Alcohol, 39(3), 525-539.

[3] Kanny, D., Brewer, R. D., Mesnick, J. B., Paulozzi, L. J., Naimi, T. S., & Lu, H. (2015). Vital signs: alcohol poisoning deaths—United States, 2010–2012. MMWR. Morbidity and mortality weekly report, 63(53), 1238.

[4] Rehm, J., Samokhvalov, A. V., & Shield, K. D. (2013). Global burden of alcoholic liver diseases. Journal of hepatology, 59(1), 160-168.

[5] Perneger, T. V., Whelton, P. K., Puddey, I. B., & Klag, M. J. (1999). Risk of end-stage renal disease associated with alcohol consumption. American journal of epidemiology, 150(12), 1275-1281.

[6] Connor, J. (2017). Alcohol consumption as a cause of cancer. Addiction, 112(2), 222-228.

[7] Barbaccia, M. L., Affricano, D., Trabucchi, M., Purdy, R. H., Colombo, G., Agabio, R., & Gessa, G. L. (1999). Ethanol markedly increases "GABAergic" neurosteroids in alcohol-preferring rats. European journal of pharmacology, 384(2-3), R1-R2.

[8] Pehrson, A. L., & Sanchez, C. (2015). Altered γ-aminobutyric acid neurotransmission in major depressive disorder: a critical review of the supporting evidence and the influence of serotonergic antidepressants. Drug design, development and therapy, 9, 603.

[9] Weiss, F., Lorang, M. T., Bloom, F. E., & Koob, G. F. (1993). Oral alcohol self-administration stimulates dopamine release in the rat nucleus accumbens: genetic and motivational determinants. Journal of Pharmacology and Experimental Therapeutics, 267(1), 250-258.

[10] Arias-Carrión, Ó., & Pöppel, E. (2007). Dopamine, learning, and reward-seeking behavior. Acta neurobiologiae experimentalis.

[11] Kelley, A. E., & Berridge, K. C. (2002). The neuroscience of natural rewards: relevance to addictive drugs. Journal of neuroscience, 22(9), 3306-3311.

[12] Bayard, M., Mcintyre, J., Hill, K. R., & Woodside Jr, J. (2004). Alcohol withdrawal syndrome. American family physician, 69(6).

[13] Gulati, A., Chandishwar, N., Shanker, K., Srimal, R. C., Dhawan, K. N., & Bhargava, K. P. (1985). Effect of alcohols on the permeability of blood-brain barrier. Pharmacological research communications, 17(1), 85-93.

[14] Nutt, D. (1999). Alcohol and the brain: pharmacological insights for psychiatrists. The British Journal of Psychiatry, 175(2), 114-119.

[15] Domingues, S. C. A., Mendonça, J. B., Laranjeira, R., & Nakamura-Palacios, E. M. (2009). Drinking and driving: a decrease in executive frontal functions in young drivers with high blood alcohol concentration. Alcohol, 43(8), 657-664.

[16] Perry, P. J., Argo, T. R., Barnett, M. J., Liesveld, J. L., Liskow, B., Hernan, J. M., ... & Brabson, M. A. (2006). The association of alcohol-induced blackouts

and grayouts to blood alcohol concentrations. Journal of forensic sciences, 51(4), 896-899.

[17] Silveri, M. M. (2012). Adolescent brain development and underage drinking in the United States: identifying risks of alcohol use in college populations. Harvard review of psychiatry, 20(4), 189-200.

[18] Peters, R., Peters, J., Warner, J., Beckett, N., & Bulpitt, C. (2008). Alcohol, dementia and cognitive decline in the elderly: a systematic review. Age and ageing, 37(5), 505-512.

[19] George, A., & Figueredo, V. M. (2011). Alcoholic cardiomyopathy: a review. Journal of cardiac failure, 17(10), 844-849.

[20] Antzelevitch, C., & Burashnikov, A. (2011). Overview of basic mechanisms of cardiac

arrhythmia. Cardiac electrophysiology clinics, 3(1), 23-45.

[21] Lieber, C. S. (2003). Relationships between nutrition, alcohol use, and liver disease. Alcohol Research and Health, 27, 220-231.

[22] Cook, R. T. (1998). Alcohol abuse, alcoholism, and damage to the immune system—a review. Alcoholism: Clinical and Experimental Research, 22(9), 1927-1942.

[23] Hurley, T. D., & Edenberg, H. J. (2012). Genes encoding enzymes involved in ethanol metabolism. Alcohol research: current reviews, 34(3), 339.

[24] Ray, L. A., & Hutchison, K. E. (2004). A polymorphism of the μ-opioid receptor gene (OPRM1) and sensitivity to the effects of alcohol in humans. Alcoholism: Clinical and Experimental

Research, 28(12), 1789-1795.

[25] Cadoret, R. J., O'Gorman, T. W., Troughton, E., & Heywood, E. (1985). Alcoholism and antisocial personality: Interrelationships, genetic and environmental factors. Archives of General Psychiatry, 42(2), 161-167.

[26] Hamdi, N. R., Krueger, R. F., & South, S. C. (2015). Socioeconomic status moderates genetic and environmental effects on the amount of alcohol use. Alcoholism: clinical and experimental research, 39(4), 603-610.

[27] Palmer, R. S., McMahon, T. J., Rounsaville, B. J., & Ball, S. A. (2010). Coercive sexual experiences, protective behavioral strategies, alcohol expectancies and consumption among male and female college students. Journal of interpersonal violence, 25(9), 1563-1578.

[28] Federation of American Societies for Experimental Biology (FASEB). (2014, April 27). Alcohol use in adolescence connected to risky behavior in adulthood. ScienceDaily.

[29] Heinz, A. J., Beck, A., Meyer-Lindenberg, A., Sterzer, P., & Heinz, A. (2011). Cognitive and neurobiological mechanisms of alcohol-related aggression. Nature Reviews Neuroscience, 12(7), 400.

[30] Pohjalainen, T., Rinne, J. O., Någren, K., Syvälahti, E., & Hietala, J. (1998). Sex differences in the striatal dopamine D2 receptor binding characteristics in vivo. American Journal of Psychiatry, 155(6), 768-773.

[31] Fillmore, M. T., & Weafer, J. (2004). Alcohol impairment of behavior in men and women.

Addiction, 99(10), 1237-1246.

[32] Eagly, A. H., & Steffen, V. J. (1986). Gender and aggressive behavior: a meta-analytic review of the social psychological literature. Psychological bulletin, 100(3), 309.

[33] Frezza, M., di Padova, C., Pozzato, G., Terpin, M., Baraona, E., & Lieber, C. S. (1990). High blood alcohol levels in women: the role of decreased gastric alcohol dehydrogenase activity and first-pass metabolism. New England Journal of Medicine, 322(2), 95-99.

[34] Jones, B. M., & Jones, M. K. (1976). Alcohol effects in women during the menstrual cycle. Annals of the New York Academy of Sciences, 273(1), 576-587.

[35] Grodstein, F., Goldman, M. B., & Cramer, D. W.

(1994). Infertility in women and moderate alcohol use. American Journal of Public Health, 84(9), 1429-1432.

[36] Bradley, K. A., Badrinath, S., Bush, K., Boyd-Wickizer, J., & Anawalt, B. (1998). Medical risks for women who drink alcohol. Journal of General Internal Medicine, 13(9), 627-639.

[37] Banakar, M. K., Kudlur, N. S., & George, S. (2009). Fetal alcohol spectrum disorder (FASD). The Indian Journal of Pediatrics, 76(11), 1173-1175.

[38] Clarren, S. K., & Smith, D. W. (1978). The fetal alcohol syndrome. New England Journal of Medicine, 298(19), 1063-1067.

[39] Grant, B. F. (1998). The impact of a family history of alcoholism on the relationship between age at onset of alcohol use and DSM-IV alcohol

dependence. Alcohol Health Res World, 22(2), 144-147.

[40] Spear, L. P. (2000). Adolescent period: Biological basis of vulnerability to develop alcoholism and other ethanol-mediated behaviors. Review of NiAAA's Neuroscience and Behavioral Research Portfolio. Bethesda, MD: National Institute on Alcohol Abuse and Alcoholism, 315-333.

The 21-Day Alcohol Switch

How To No Longer Be A Slave To Alcohol And Your Life Revolving Around It

By

Patrick Dickinson

Introduction

According to the 2015 National Survey on Drug Use and Health, 15.1 million adults over the age of 18 (more than 6% of this age group) have an alcohol use disorder. Additionally, an estimated 88,000 people die from alcohol-related causes annually. How many of these people know they have a problem with alcohol abuse but don't take any steps to remedy the situation, simply choosing instead to become another preventable statistic?

Overcoming an alcohol addiction may seem like an impossible task, but this is simply not true. By following the steps laid out in this book, you can completely change your relationship with alcohol and no longer be a slave to the drug. The expert advice provided here comes from years of experience in struggling with and eventually beating alcohol addiction. Freeing yourself from alcohol isn't necessarily easy, but it is certainly not impossible, either.

Living without alcohol, even for just 21 days, can have incredible effects on your body and mind. You will learn more about yourself in this three-week period than you may have in many years, particularly when it comes to your strength of character, and how you deal with challenging situations. What's more, the physical improvements you see will be pronounced – your skin will improve, you will lose weight, you'll feel infinitely healthier, and you could even be adding years to your life. People won't recognize you after the 21-day challenge, and you may not even recognize yourself.

Have you tried to give up alcohol in the past, but haven't succeeded? It's not an easy thing to do and requires a lot of willpower and planning. Blindly attempting to quit alcohol rarely works out, and can make you less likely to attempt to quit again in the future. The knowledge and information contained in this book will set you on the right track for success when it comes to beating alcohol addiction. It is a powerful resource that will help you overcome your darkest days, your biggest hurdles, and your most difficult challenges. By following the advice in this book, you can beat alcohol and change your life forever.

Every day of drinking alcohol is a day of decreasing your liver function, pumping your body full of toxins, causing irreversible damage to your skin, gaining weight, harming your brain, and wasting money. There is never a better time than the present to take charge of your circumstances, stop making excuses, and beat alcohol once and for all. Even if you decide to return to drinking after three weeks, the challenge will completely change your relationship with alcohol. Alcohol will no longer run your life, control your decision making, or destroy your body.

Don't waste the best years of your life drowning in hangovers and regrets. Take the first step to change – read this book today.

1. Making The Decision To Drink Less Alcohol

Every day, people around the world wake up and vow never to drink alcohol again. Some may make the decision due to a recent medical diagnosis, while others are trying to make a lifestyle change or doing it for religious reasons. Sometimes, all it takes is a particularly bad hangover to turn you off alcohol for life. Whatever the reason, there is never a bad time to assess your relationship with alcohol and determine whether or not you are in control of your drinking habits.

Why Drinking Alcohol Makes Us Feel So Good

Alcohol can encourage us to behave in less than savory ways. By taking away our inhibitions, even a small amount of alcohol can make us act in ways we would not normally dream of. Despite being a depressant, the immediate effects of alcohol are to improve our confidence, enhance our mood, and turn even the most introverted person into a social butterfly. One of the key dangers of alcohol consumption is that it increases our likelihood to participate in "risk-taking" behavior, such as feeling that we are fine to drive home after a night of drinking, or initiating a conversation with someone way out of our league.

Similarly, alcohol can help to distract ourselves from aspects of life that we may not want to deal with. Whether it's an emotional issue like a relationship break up or the loss of a loved one, or a general feeling of sadness or dissatisfaction with our lives, alcohol can help us to forget the things that make life so hard. Of course, one of the big problems with this is that we forget how to deal with some of the more challenging aspects of life and lose our natural coping mechanisms. Many people turn to alcohol as a way to deal with the many ups and downs life brings with it; although it may feel like a solution in the short term, it actually tends to make things harder in the long run.

How Alcohol Changes Our Brains

Have you ever wondered how alcohol can alter our behavior so dramatically? Where that feeling of courage comes from after a few drinks? Why you crave a drink after a long day at work? Why it feels so good when you open a bottle of wine on a Friday night? There is still a lot that scientists don't understand about alcohol and its effects on the brain, but as more research has been performed in recent years, some of the pathways through which alcohol acts have been understood in more detail.

Alcohol interacts with numerous neurotransmitters in the brain, either up-regulating or down-regulating their levels, which alters our mood and behavior. In a study testing the immediate effects of alcohol consumption on mice, it was shown that alcohol significantly increased the amount of the neurotransmitter GABA in the brain[2]. GABA has many roles and functions in the brain, and one of those roles is to reduce levels of stress, anxiety, depression, and pain [23]. So, when we drink alcohol, our GABA levels increase and our feelings of stress and anxiety are reduced, which is one of the reasons why alcohol makes us feel so good.

Another study using mice to evaluate the effects of alcohol showed that immediately after alcohol consumption, dopamine was released in the brain[33]. When we do something our brain thinks is good for us, such as taking a drink of water when we are thirsty, our brain releases dopamine as a "reward". The release of dopamine results in feelings of pleasure, and is designed to act as positive reinforcement – we have done something that is good for us, and our brain wants to make sure we do it again and again[1].

Alcohol hijacks this pathway and results in a

dopamine boost that's usually significantly stronger than the amount our brain would normally release[15]. It isn't long before our brains start to associate alcohol consumption with feelings of pleasure, and this is what forms the basis for alcohol abuse and addiction. This is the reason why many of us crave alcohol, or become dependent on it to feel good. It is a very strong pathway, and a very difficult cycle to break.

It is possible to develop an alcohol dependency without even realizing it is happening to you. By periodically taking a break from alcohol, you can ensure that you are in control of your drinking and aren't becoming dependent on alcohol. Doing the 21-day alcohol-free challenge is a great way to keep your drinking in check and ensure your relationship with alcohol is safe and healthy.

The Health Benefits Of Taking A Break From Alcohol

Of course, the addictive nature of alcohol is just one of its many downsides. Alcohol doesn't only affect our mind, but has significant impacts on our bodies too. Long-term alcohol use has been strongly linked to serious health conditions including liver disease[6], cardiovascular disease[14], increased risk of stroke[12], increased risk of numerous cancers[31], and many more detrimental health conditions.

Many people quit drinking when they are diagnosed with a disease that may be linked to or worsened by alcohol consumption. Unfortunately, in some cases, the damage is already done. The best way to protect your health when it comes to the effects of alcohol is to cut out or cut back your consumption to a healthy level. This 21-day alcohol-free challenge is a great way to do just that.

So, how much alcohol is too much? The CDC

currently recommends that alcohol be consumed in moderation, which they define as up to one alcoholic drink per day for women, and up to two alcoholic drinks per day for men. Over a week, these guidelines extend to up to 11 drinks for women or 17 drinks for men. One drink is defined as one 12-oz beer, one 5-oz glass of wine, or a 1.5-oz shot of distilled spirits or liquor. The one-to-two drinks per day rule does not mean that you can skip alcohol for five days and then consume eight drinks in one night, as binge drinking is far worse for your health than drinking in moderation.

Many people exceed the recommended alcohol intake from time to time. Having three drinks on a special occasion isn't going to have a serious effect on your health, but doing it regularly may. By reducing your alcohol consumption to a safe level, you will have more energy, sleep better, reduce your risk of numerous health conditions, and, most importantly – feel as though you are in charge of your drinking.

If you or someone you know has a serious problem with alcohol addiction, you should contact a medical professional as soon as possible so that immediate action can be taken. However, if you just feel like you drink too much and want to take a break, or are looking to give up alcohol for good, keep reading to see how the 21-day alcohol-free challenge might be just what you have been looking for.

2. What To Know Before Starting Your 21-Day Challenge

It's important not to dive immediately into the 21-day alcohol-free challenge. If you suddenly decide to stop drinking without thinking the decision through or doing the appropriate planning, the chances are that you will not succeed. You need to ensure that you are both physically and mentally prepared for this journey before it begins.

One of the first decisions you need to make is whether you are hoping to cut back on the amount of alcohol you are drinking, or cut alcohol out of your life completely. Reducing your drinking may be sufficient if you are hoping to make a healthier lifestyle change or save some money. It can definitely improve your relationship with alcohol and also act as a proactive first step towards cutting alcohol out of your life for good.

Many people who decide to reduce their drinking rather than eliminate it completely find it easier to stick to their alcohol consumption goals than those who give up alcohol entirely. By allowing yourself two alcoholic drinks per week, you can reward yourself for your hard work and not feel as though you are missing out. Plus, it allows you to use alcohol just as a "treat" on special occasions, rather than something that you rely on to get through each day.

Why It's Important To Stay Social

Allowing yourself to drink once or twice a week ensures that you can participate in social drinking. For many people, drinking is a social activity, and if you stop drinking entirely and don't want to put yourself in situations where alcohol is being consumed, it can have a huge impact on your social life. Drinking occasionally (and in moderation) with friends can be a healthy activity, and it's certainly important to keep your social life active even when you're not drinking, or trying to drink less.

In a study that surveyed adults aged 45 years or older, a correlation was found between loneliness and alcohol abuse[34]. It was hypothesized that lonely people were more likely to consume alcohol in excess because they didn't have a social outlet, and weren't as easily able to vent about their days or unwind with friends. Similarly, studies have shown that social drinkers earn more money (on average) than those who do not drink. One study reported that males who frequent bars at least once per month earn 7% more than those who do not[24].

How To Reduce Your Alcohol Consumption

Do you believe that you can limit your drinking to one to two drinks per week, or only drink on predetermined occasions such as when you are out with friends? If so, this may be a great way to improve your physical health and ensure you are in control of your drinking, without sacrificing your social life. Cutting back on your alcohol consumption might be easier than you think – you just need to set yourself specific goals and rules.

For example, if you usually drink every day, start by designating two days a week where you will NOT drink. It may feel strange at first, and you will instinctively want to pour yourself a drink when you get home from work. Many people find that substituting a non-alcoholic beverage such as flavored sparkling water helps them feel as though they are drinking, without the alcohol content. Try not to replace your alcohol consumption with soda, as the sugar and caffeine content of most sodas means that you won't experience many of the health benefits of giving up drinking.

Once you have succeeded in incorporating alcohol-free days into your routine, increase the number of them until you are only drinking 1-2 days per week.

After several months, you will likely be less dependent on alcohol, crave it less, and be less likely to turn to it after a bad day at work. You will feel proud of the progress you have made, and when you start to see the physical health benefits and the money you are saving, you'll never want to return to your old drinking habits again!

In a study of British adults who significantly reduced their alcohol consumption for just one month, 80% of people felt in control of their drinking and over 70% reported realizing that they didn't need a drink to enjoy themselves[8]. What's more, 70% reported improved general health, better sleep, and increased energy levels. More than 50% had lost weight, reported improved concentration, and had better skin. These findings show that reducing your alcohol intake can have a huge immediate effect on your health and wellbeing.

However, not everyone can easily reduce their

alcohol intake, and having one drink can so often lead to many more. If this is the case, you may be better off by removing alcohol from your life completely. The 21-day alcohol-free challenge is a great place to start your alcohol-free journey.

The Best Tips For Alcohol-Free Success

Nobody said that giving up alcohol was easy – everybody would do it if it was simple. It's a tough challenge that requires a lot of inner strength and willpower and some help along the way from those closest to you. However, there are a few tips you can follow that will make your transition into an alcohol-free lifestyle go much more smoothly:

1. Tell Your Family And Friends

The most important thing to remember is never to be ashamed or embarrassed about what you are doing. Removing alcohol from your life doesn't mean you have an addiction or are weak; in fact, it is the opposite of that. It means you are making healthy lifestyle changes, and are strong enough to make a difficult decision because you know it is the right thing to do in the long run.

Many individuals worry about what their friends and family will think of them and their decision to quit drinking. However, when you tell your loved ones you are taking a break from alcohol, and explain to them your reasons why, chances are they will be nothing but enthusiastic and supportive of your decision. You will be more likely to stick to your goals if you have shared them with the people closest to you, and you can share your achievements and successes with them along the way.

What's more, by being honest with the people around you, they will understand why you have been turning down happy hour invitations, and it may encourage them to find non-drinking related activities that you can all enjoy – this plays back into the importance of maintaining your social life. Constantly reminding those around you that you want to stop drinking (and your reasons why) also acts as a reminder for yourself and improves your chances of alcohol-free success.

You may even be able to convince someone to join you on this journey. Giving up alcohol with a friend can greatly increase your chances of success and make the process more fun along the way. You can share your struggles and triumphs together, find social activities that don't involve drinking, and marvel over how much money you are both saving.

2. Avoid Tempting Situations

For the first several days of your alcohol-free challenge, it's a good idea to avoid situations where alcohol is being consumed. Your mind will be most susceptible and most vulnerable to relapse for the first 2-3 days, as the powers of addiction will still have a strong hold on you. While it may seem like you are missing out on spending time with your friends or family, or feeling left out that you can't attend social drinks with your colleagues after work, remember that it is only temporary until you have had some time to adjust to your new lifestyle.

If you tend to drink while you are eating out, it might be a good idea to find some restaurants that don't serve alcohol. Similarly, if you drink while watching bands or sports games, you may want to avoid these activities for the first week or so of your 21-day challenge. You could replace these activities with a trip to the cinema, or a game of tennis. If you do decide to go out with friends or family, volunteering to drive is a great way to ensure you say sober for the night. If you tend to pour yourself a drink as soon as you get home, try going for a walk instead. This will help you to unwind from your day in a much healthier way and also ensure you get some exercise that will release endorphins and give you a natural high[10].

Of course, the thought of never being able to go to a restaurant that serves alcohol, or not being able to go to the bar for a game of pool with your friends doesn't sound very appealing. Luckily, it may only be for the first week or so of your journey that you need to remove yourself from these situations. Once you feel as though you are more in control of your drinking, it's important that you try to re-introduce some of these social behaviors into your life.

Author and addiction specialist Allen Carr[7] states in his EasyWay method that beating alcohol addiction doesn't require willpower or the need to remove yourself from situations where alcohol is present. Instead, he focuses on changing your attitude towards drinking, understanding your addiction, and freeing yourself from the constraints of it. Once you become comfortable with your addiction, it is easier to manage and overcome, and you can still have fun and do the things you enjoy.

3. Identify Triggers

It is important that you learn to identify your triggers – the thoughts or feelings that lead you to crave alcohol. For many people, a trigger might be a stressful day at work or an argument with a loved one. If you can identify these triggers, you can take the necessary precautions (such as going for a walk or calling a friend to vent) rather than turning to alcohol.

Identifying your triggers is a key component to your success, particularly if you have tried unsuccessfully to quit alcohol in the past. Try to identify the moments or feelings where temptation got the better of you and you succumbed to alcohol. Perhaps it was because you still had alcohol easily accessible in your house, or because it was easy to stop at a bar on your way home from work. If you have tried unsuccessfully to quit drinking in the past, do not be discouraged – your experiences will make you more prepared this time around and give you the upper hand against alcohol.

4. Reward Your Progress

Throughout this journey, it is important to recognize your achievements, no matter how small, and reward yourself accordingly. Similarly, don't be too hard on yourself if you slip up once in a while. Making a drastic lifestyle change such as this one is not without its challenges, and you are bound to make mistakes along the way. As long as you learn from them, move on and stick to your goals as best you can, you're doing great. One of the best ways to stick to your goals is to break them down into short-term achievements. Reward yourself when you have completed three alcohol-free days, then one week, then two weeks. Use the money you are saving to buy yourself a new outfit, or plan a spa day with some friends. You'll be surprised by how quickly your savings accumulate, so don't be afraid to treat yourself every now and again.

How To Get The Most From Your 21-Day Alcohol-Free Challenge

Giving up alcohol might seem like an impossible task, but it's important to remember that this challenge is only for 21 days. If you live to be 70 years old, this represents 0.08% of your life. Put into perspective like this, it's really not a long time to go without alcohol at all. What's more, this challenge could have a huge impact on your whole relationship with alcohol and completely change your drinking habits.

It is absolutely worth throwing everything you have into this 0.08% of your life. Regardless of whether you are giving up alcohol in pursuit of a healthier diet, or for charity, or because a loved one suggested you do it together, you'll feel such a strong sense of self-satisfaction at the end of the 21-day challenge. You'll be able to look in the mirror and know that you have experienced life without alcohol. From here, you can either continue on your sobriety journey or return to a safe level of social drinking. The important thing is that the choice will be up to you, as you will now be in control of alcohol in your life.

Before you start the 21-day challenge, there are two things you should do. The first is to take a photo of yourself on the morning of your first alcohol-free day. This will be a great reference point for you to track your progress from and look back on as you progress through the challenge. Many people find that having a reference point, such as a "before" photograph, makes their progress feel more real and is a great motivator to continue the journey. After the 21 days are up, you may be surprised by just how different you look. You may notice changes in your eyes and the shape of your face, the clarity of your skin, and your overall body tone and shape. If you continue your alcohol-free journey beyond the three-week mark, these changes will become more and more pronounced.

After just three alcohol-free weeks, many people see dramatic changes in their facial skin. Alcohol tends to make people look older, in part because it causes tissue inflammation, which is what causes the red, flushed look when drinking. Although the redness usually subsides once the alcohol leaves your system, long term drinking can cause permanent skin damage[21]. After just 21 days, you will notice decreased redness in your face, a reduced presence of blood vessels, and improved elasticity of the skin.

There are many other benefits that you may be surprised to see after just 21 days of going without alcohol. It is highly likely that you will lose weight, as alcohol is very calorie-dense. This will, of course, be more pronounced if you replace your Friday night trip to the bar with a brisk walk around the block, or arrange a social tennis match with friends instead of a wine tasting afternoon. Alcohol also weakens the immune system, so you will likely see improved immunity and not get sick as often[30]. Of course, there are numerous other health benefits of reducing your alcohol intake, and each person has a different journey. This is a key reason why you should start a progress tracker.

As well as taking a "before" photo, keep a progress tracker throughout your alcohol-free journey to act as a record for how far you've come. Include the following categories: quality of sleep, appetite, happiness, productivity, motivation, and energy levels. At the end of each day, rate each of these categories on a scale of 1-10, where 1 is poor and 10 is excellent. You will be able to track improvements in sleep, energy levels, and more. Include a section for comments, as well as an area to record your weight each day. Make sure you weigh yourself at the same time of day each day, as our weights fluctuate throughout the day.

It is important to remember that the 21-day "challenge" is indeed a challenge. Looking at before and after pictures only shows the tip of the iceberg of your alcohol-free journey, and there will be a lot of difficult times in between. Alcohol withdrawals are no joke, and can be the reason why many people don't make it through the first several days of quitting alcohol. This is why you need to do everything you can to prepare for the challenges of the 21-day alcohol-free challenge.

3. How To Prepare For The Alcohol-Free Challenge

Preparation is key when it comes to succeeding in beating alcohol. You need to be aware of all the challenges you will experience along the way, and develop strategies to cope with each of them. Do your research and learn what to expect when you give up alcohol, and accept that it may take more than a month to prepare fully for your journey. A spur of the moment decision to give up alcohol, with little to no preparation, will likely not result in success. Following the advice in this chapter gives you the best possible chance of enjoying an alcohol-free lifestyle, and will help your challenge go as smoothly as possible.

How To Know When You're Ready To Quit

Making the decision to give up alcohol should not come lightly. It is a huge, personal decision, and one that you need to be fully committed to. In order to be successful, you need to be 100% certain that this is the path you want to take, and fully immerse yourself into the process of giving up alcohol for 21 days. To prepare for this challenge, follow the steps below.

Write Down Your Reasons For Quitting

This will ensure that you are completely clear on why you are giving up alcohol, and will serve as a record you can look at if/when things start to get really tough during your challenge. Take the time to find your reasons for quitting alcohol, and include any consequences and drawbacks that you experience when you drink alcohol. Consider the effects that alcohol has on your physical health, your mental wellbeing, your relationships with friends and family, and your performance at work.

It may help to write a list of pros and cons. You can list positive aspects of drinking alcohol, such as immediate feelings of happiness or an improved social life, and weigh them against the cons, such as feeling terrible the next day, and the financial burden of drinking regularly. For most people, creating a list of pros and cons shows them how much sense it makes to give up alcohol, and can be a valuable asset to look back on when you are struggling through the 21-day challenge. It can also help you explain why you are not drinking to those around you.

You may also want to write down some of the more embarrassing or sad experiences you have had while drinking. Whether it was embarrassing yourself at a party or blacking out and not remembering how you got home, having these stories on paper will show you that the effects of alcohol can be very real and very scary, and remind you why you are not drinking. Write down how you felt the next day, and use it as motivation to ensure you never experience those levels of regret or shame from alcohol again.

Discuss Your Decision With Your Doctor

Many of us are not honest about our alcohol consumption when it comes to talking to medical professionals. However, if you are making the decision to quit alcohol, it is essential that you have an honest conversation with your doctor first. If you choose to start the path to recovery alone and in your home, you need to be very aware that the effects of alcohol withdrawal can be potentially life-threatening. Ensure that you have a friend or family member who will be able to check on you very regularly, especially for the first week.

When it comes to alcohol withdrawals, the severity of your symptoms will usually correspond with the amount you had been regularly drinking. Heavy drinkers and long-term alcoholics typically experience very severe withdrawal symptoms. Some of the most serious symptoms are listed below. If you experience any of these symptoms during your alcohol-free challenge, it is imperative that you seek medical assistance immediately:

- **Panic Attacks** – panic attacks can be brought on both by alcohol consumption and alcohol withdrawal[11]. Symptoms of a panic attack include shaking, heart palpitations, sweating, and a deep sense of dread. This can be a very serious condition and may cause individuals to act irrationally.

- **Severe Anxiety** – Alcohol and anxiety are strongly linked. While in the short term, alcohol use can reduce anxiety, it can increase feelings of anxiousness in the long term. During the early stages of alcohol withdrawal, intense anxiety may be experienced as a result of the changing levels of dopamine in the brain. These feelings of anxiousness often encourage people to drink and derail their efforts to give up alcohol.

- **The Shakes** – The shakes, or tremors, is a common symptom during alcohol withdrawal, and one of the earliest symptoms shown. One of the effects of alcohol is to slow down the brain and reduce excitatory neuronal activity; this is why alcohol is known as a "depressant". To compensate for this change, the brain releases more excitatory signals[16]. During alcohol withdrawal, the depressant effects of alcohol are no longer present, but the brain is still pumping out excitatory signals. This leads to the body being in a temporarily "amped up" state, and is what causes tremors.

- **Rapid Heart Rate** – An increase in heart rate (tachycardia) occurs in the same way that tremors do, but can be a much more serious symptom. Increases in heart rate can lead to arrhythmias, or irregular heartbeats, which can, in turn, cause a heart attack. If you feel your heart rate increase or your heartbeat feels irregular, seek medical help immediately.

Is It Safe To Quit Drinking At Home?

The severity of the alcohol withdrawal symptoms you will experience depends on the severity of the addiction in the first place. If you drank heavily, and for a long time, your withdrawal symptoms will likely be more intense and severe. This is why it is essential to be honest with your doctor about how much you are drinking – they need to know if it's even safe for you to give up drinking in your own home, largely unsupervised.

Of course, although it is challenging, many people are able to quit drinking with relatively few or no severe symptoms. However, alcohol withdrawal should not be taken lightly and can be life-threatening if not monitored or appropriately treated. Approximately 5-10% of people who withdraw from alcohol develop delirium tremens, or alcohol withdrawal syndrome[3]. This is a life-threatening condition that can lead to seizures if untreated. If you are at risk of developing delirium tremens, you need to give up alcohol in a medical facility rather than at home.

Remember, you are not on this journey alone. Your friends and family will be supportive of your cause and no doubt be on hand to assist you, however you need it. Similarly, medical professionals will do whatever they can to help you quit drinking, as they understand the health benefits of quitting and the immense risk factors that drinking alcohol brings with it. Medical help makes quitting alcohol significantly easier, as many doctors prescribe benzodiazepines to treat the symptoms of alcohol withdrawal. Benzodiazepines are relatively safe but can be addictive, so should only be taken for a short amount of time while the symptoms of withdrawal are at their worst, and only under strict medical guidance[29].

How To Change Your Attitude Towards Alcohol

Another key to success when it comes to giving up alcohol is to change your view on drinking. It is important to remember that you are not losing a friend here, or giving up something you love (like ice cream or chocolate). You may feel that you love alcohol, but really you just depend on it. It is bad for your health, it affects your decision making, it costs you money, and it can make you do stupid things. Alcohol sounds like the worst friend you've ever had, and by realizing that it is the enemy, your path to giving it up becomes much more straightforward.

By getting to a point where you don't want alcohol in your life, you will have the willpower to finally rid yourself of the vice-like grip it has over you. Your decision to quit should fill you with relief and excitement about your alcohol-free life ahead. You won't waste time in bed with bad hangovers, you'll feel healthier and want to be more active, and you will have a better overall relationship with your mind, body and soul. Reaching this mindset before you give up alcohol will do wonders for your booze-free journey and the success you see whilst on it.

How To Prepare For The Day You Quit

There's no denying that the first several alcohol-free days are the most difficult. You need to be as mentally prepared as possible in order to succeed. It is important to choose a date in advance that will be your first alcohol-free day and discuss this date with your doctor. Some people like to choose a date that is significant to them, and others seek the advice of a doctor to choose their date. If you drink heavily, you will need to choose a date that gives you some time to try to cut back on your alcohol consumption first, as going from heavy drinking to no drinking is difficult, painful, and dangerous.

Another important preparation step is to remove all

alcohol from your house. You can give it to a friend or family member, or simply throw it away. Just because you are having friends over for dinner doesn't mean you need to be able to have beers in the fridge to offer them – they will understand and be supportive of your decision. Instead, replace the alcohol in your house with flavored sparkling water alternatives or low-calorie sodas. You can even get creative with alcohol-free drinks such as virgin cocktails. These types of drinks can be helpful during the initial phases of your 21-day challenge, as you can almost trick your mind into thinking you have a drink in hand. You may also want to stock up on comfort foods to treat yourself with when you can't have a drink.

One final key component to your preparation is to understand the effects that giving up alcohol will have on your body. You will likely be highly emotional, have a very disrupted sleep schedule, be unable to eat at times and ravenously hungry at other times, and probably just not know how to feel a lot of the time. This is all very new for your brain and your body, and you ultimately just have to go with the ebb and flow and let your body feel how it is going to feel. Sleep when you can, eat whatever sounds good when it sounds good, don't be too hard on yourself, and reach out for help when you need it.

It is very important to remove yourself from people or situations that are likely to make you drink. Until you have developed the willpower to say no, these situations are a recipe for disaster when it comes to maintaining your sobriety. You may have friends that you really only catch up with when you are drinking – perhaps it will be too tempting to be around them until you are in control of your drinking. However, it can be quite a revelation to find out that these friends were really only drinking because you wanted to, or were drinking significantly less than you without you realizing.

If you have a particular friend who likes to host boozy

dinner parties, maybe skip the next one. If you have an annual camping trip coming up that usually involves alcohol, don't go this year. The most important thing during this period is protecting your sobriety, and not doing anything that could jeopardize your progress.

4. How To Survive Your First Alcohol-Free Day

So, the big day has finally arrived. After months of preparation, you are now starting your journey of sobriety. For some people, the first day is the hardest. For others, the worst of the symptoms don't kick in until days two or three. Regardless of when it really starts to hit, your first day of sobriety is never easy. Remember to take a "before" picture in the morning to monitor physical changes, and also fill out your progress tracker to analyze your journey. This will be one of the hardest periods of your life, but with all the preparation you have put into it, and with the right people around you, success is just around the corner.

If you don't drink heavily every day, your first 24 hours won't physically be too difficult. If you do drink heavily, this may be a different story. The most common side effects you are likely to experience are sweating, a rapid heart rate, changes in blood pressure, shaking or tremors, headaches, nausea or vomiting, agitation, anxiety or restlessness, and a fever[9]. In all, the symptoms during the first 24 hours of alcohol withdrawal can feel a bit like a hangover. If you experience anything more serious, such as heart palpitations, contact a medical professional immediately.

For the first few days, distracting yourself from alcohol is very important. Your mind will be consumed by the fact that you haven't had a drink, and you will definitely miss something that was such a dominant part of your daily lifestyle. In this chapter, we will discuss what to expect during your first alcohol-free day and the best ways in which you can distract yourself from alcohol during the first day of your journey, ensuring that you get off to the best possible start to the 21-day challenge.

Why It's Important To Change Up Your Routine

Firstly, it is essential that you don't rely on your usual routine to get you through the day. You'll need to change things up so that you don't focus on the fact that you're not drinking. If your usual routine is to pour yourself a drink as soon as you get home after work, delay the time you will arrive home as much as you can. Stay at work and catch up on an unfinished project, then stop at the park on your drive home. If it's a nice evening, you can even take a book with you and read for an hour or so until you venture home.

If you have friends or family nearby, you may want to visit them on your first day to spend the evening catching up and not thinking about your new alcohol-free life. Some people even like to spend their first few sober nights staying with a family member if it is convenient – this takes you out of your regular setting, distracts you from alcohol, and also provides you with someone who can check up on you or offer you help and support when you need it.

Another effective way to distract yourself from drinking is to use a diary to plan activities and appointments with friends. If you keep yourself busy with social engagements, such as meeting a friend after work to go swimming, you will spend less time thinking about alcohol. Similarly, you can use these 21 days to find a new hobby. You could try learning a musical instrument or painting. If you sign up for a weekly class that begins on your fist alcohol-free day, you will have the perfect distraction to keep your mind off alcohol.

How To Adjust Your Diet To Suit An Alcohol-Free Lifestyle

Eating healthily is very important during your alcohol-free journey. Heavy drinking puts enormous strain on your body, and often goes hand in hand with poor nutrition. Studies have shown that alcohol consumption decreases appetite, promotes poor nutritional choices, and displaces other foods from the diet[20]. What's more, alcohol interferes with the absorption and utilization of many nutrients[13]. This means that even if you are eating nutrient-rich foods and lots of fresh vegetables and fruits, regular heavy drinking counteracts this and can even lead to malnutrition.

When you give up alcohol, you'll have more time and energy to put into planning and cooking good meals, and your body will finally be able to make the most of the nutrients you give it. Making sure you have a well-stocked pantry, and putting time into meal planning for the week are great activities to take your mind off drinking. When you get home after your first alcohol-free day, cutting up vegetables and making a healthy stir fry can be a very therapeutic (and delicious) way to unwind after work.

If there are certain foods that you usually associate with alcohol, you may want to avoid these. For example, if you always have a beer with pizza, don't eat pizza for your first week or so of the 21-day challenge. You may find that sobriety increases your appetite, or you may find that you don't really feel hungry at all. Just eat when it feels right, and try to fuel your body with nutrient-rich foods such as vegetables and fruits, complex carbohydrates and grains like brown rice, pasta and quinoa, and lean protein options like fish, chicken, beans, and nuts.

If eating food reduces your craving for a drink, eat more of it. Remember that alcohol is very calorie-dense, so by no longer drinking, your body is not getting as many calories as it is used to. Even if you eat more during each day of the challenge, it is still likely that you will lose weight. Don't be afraid to eat whenever you are hungry, and treat yourself (especially on your first day!) to some special foods that you wouldn't normally have.

In addition to eating well, make sure that you are

staying hydrated during the first day of your challenge. As someone who is giving up alcohol, it is likely that you know how a hangover feels. Drinking water when you are hungover aids your recovery and always helps you to feel better, and it has exactly the same effect when you are withdrawing from alcohol. Many people sweat when they are withdrawing from alcohol, which can lead to further dehydration. Water will hydrate you, improve your kidney and liver function, and help to flush toxins from your system as quickly as possible.

It is recommended that men drink 12 cups or 3 liters of water per day, and women drink 9 cups or 2.2 liters per day. However, during alcohol withdrawals, you may require even more water than this. If you start to feel thirsty, you are already dehydrated. As an alternative to regular tap water, you may want to drink sparkling water, or even flavored sparkling water. These offer more taste, and the carbonation almost makes you feel as though you are drinking alcohol. When you are first transitioning to an alcohol-free lifestyle, they are a great alternative to a boozy beverage.

How To Ensure You're Ready For Day Two

Making it through your first night won't be an easy task; you will likely be restless and unable to sleep. Insomnia or disrupted sleep might be a symptom that you experience for the entire length of the 21-day challenge[5], and even for months after you quit drinking. You may want to consider taking melatonin or another natural sleep aid, and getting as much exercise as possible. For your first night, just sleep as much as you can. Set the alarm for early in the morning (something you should start to do on a regular basis to help regulate your sleep schedule), and try to get in the habit of waking up and getting moving early. This will make you more tired in the evening and hopefully improve your ability to fall asleep at night.

If you're worried about making it through your first night sober, schedule an early morning workout for the next day. Obviously, you're not going to go from being a heavy drinker to a gym junkie overnight, but by making an appointment with a personal trainer, you have a commitment that you have to keep. Make sure you pay in advance – the fact that you have already spent money will make you far more likely to show up! If gyms and personal trainers aren't your style, see if you can convince a friend to go on a pre-work brisk walk with you. If you've been drinking heavily, early mornings probably aren't something you're very familiar with. However, there's something very refreshing about starting the day with a brisk walk, and early mornings are a time when the world is quiet and still. Give it a try, and you might just learn to like it.

5. How To Cruise Through Your First Week Without Alcohol

Waking up in the morning after surviving your first 24 hours alcohol-free can be a surreal experience. Hopefully, you managed to get some sleep and woke up to your new best friend, the alarm clock. You'll probably be feeling a bit strange – some of the withdrawal symptoms will be at their worst today, and it's likely that you didn't get the best sleep. Just power through today and know that once you do, you'll be through the worst phase of acute alcohol withdrawals. That wasn't so bad, was it?

Top Tips For Surviving Day Two

Now that you have made it through the dreaded first 24 hours, you are hopefully feeling inspired and ready for day two. Many people find that by this stage, they're ready to make the most of their positive momentum and undertake other health kicks. For example, you're already using this time to help your liver by replacing alcohol with water. The toxins that build up in your liver will gradually be flushed out, and you'll feel a lot better because of it. However, you could feel even better by incorporating some detoxifying smoothies and juices into your diet.

Starting the day with a superfood smoothie was likely not on your radar at all a month ago, but now that you've kicked the alcohol habit, why not go one step further and make this a three-week period where you really focus hard on your physical health and wellbeing? Incorporate vegetables such as carrots and spinach into a smoothie, and use citrus fruits or bananas for taste. Beet juice is actually more delicious than you would expect and has been shown to have a powerful detoxification effect on the liver[17]. It takes some getting used to, but you'll be amazed by how good you start to feel and how much energy you have throughout the day when you start it with a nutrient-filled smoothie. You'll be able to wave goodbye to morning headaches, drowsiness that lasts until well after your second cup of coffee, irritability and nausea. Before too long, you'll be wondering how you even survived with your old lifestyle and feeling so terrible all the time.

As well as incorporating some high-nutrient foods into your diet, start thinking about exercising more. This will do wonders for keeping your mind occupied, reducing your stress levels, and distracting you from any thoughts of alcohol. Plus, if you're having trouble sleeping now that you're not drinking, exercise will help to tire you out so you can sleep right through the night and wake up feeling refreshed and ready to go.

Many people who have issues with alcohol addiction and dependency actually find that they can channel their addictive personality and use it for good. It only takes a little bit of exercise for your brain to become hooked on the endorphins, and then you'll want it more and more and more. Going for that first jog around the block is always the hardest, but you'll feel great afterward and want to push yourself to go further and do better the next time you go. If you can stick to eating mostly healthy foods and exercising regularly, you won't even be able to recognize yourself at the end of the three-week challenge!

Another thing you can try to do to improve your overall health is to start going to bed earlier. Your circadian rhythm will likely be disturbed from the sudden lack of alcohol in your system, so you may feel tired at strange times, or all the time, or not at all. Even if you're not tired by 10pm, going to bed earlier will help your body reset its circadian rhythm and also make it easier for you to wake up in the morning. Rest and relaxation can be almost as good as sleep, so curl up in bed with a good book and just see if you can fall asleep. Try to avoid using your phone or other screens too much as these can actually activate certain parts of the brain and make us feel more awake – stick to reading a book or listening to a podcast. If you used to drink late into the night, going to bed earlier will take away a lot of the temptation you may feel, and help your transition to an alcohol-free lifestyle.

However, it doesn't all have to be about kale and kickboxing. Make sure you're not too hard on yourself if you can't stomach a spinach smoothie on day two, or don't feel like going on a one-mile jog. Remember, it's only your second day into sobriety, and you've already made a lot of great progress by saying no to alcohol and taking the first steps towards becoming a better, healthier, more in-control version of yourself. Take the challenge at your own pace, and look after your body as best you can. Your main priority is to stay sober for 21 days, not to become a bodybuilder in this time!

Make sure you reward the progress you have made, no matter how small it may seem. Our brains are heavily wired towards positive reinforcement, so any sort of "treat" you offer yourself will make you feel a lot better and do wonders for your chances of staying on an alcohol-free path. A treat can be whatever you feel like; maybe you want to let yourself have ice-cream for dinner on day two of the challenge (why not?!), or buy that new pair of shoes you were thinking about. You're saving a lot of money by not drinking, so don't be afraid to splurge and treat yourself to something nice – you deserve it.

Of course, you have to remember that it's only day two, and even though you've made great progress, there's still a long way to go in the challenge. Don't put yourself in a risky situation as your mind will still be vulnerable to the pull of alcohol. Stay away from bars and booze-loving friends for at least a few more days until you are more in control of your relationship with alcohol. Also, remember to keep filling out your progress tracker each day as the challenge progresses to monitor the headway you are making towards beating alcohol.

How To Wave Goodbye To Withdrawal Symptoms

By your third day, you will definitely be through the worst of the physical symptoms of alcohol withdrawal. If you're honest with yourself, how was it? Was it easier or more difficult than you expected? Even though you had planned and researched thoroughly, was there anything about the withdrawal process that surprised you? Take some notes in your progress tracker to sum up your first alcohol-free 48 hours. Hopefully, there are many more to come!

On the third day of the challenge, many people find that their only physical symptoms remaining are some tremors, light sweating, and general fatigue (this will be intensified if you haven't been sleeping well). If you're still experiencing intense headaches, nausea/vomiting, heart palpitations, or anxiety/paranoia, you should check in with your doctor to make sure that everything is okay. Otherwise, you should be ready to tackle day three with a strong sense of self-achievement already.

While the physical symptoms may be subsiding, sometimes the third day can be when it really gets mentally tough to refrain from drinking. You've made it through a couple of days without alcohol, you're starting to feel good about it, but you're probably also starting to miss it. Now that you've come this far and done all the hard work, it's important not to have a lapse in concentration or lose your way and slip back into the comfort of alcohol. Remember what it is that you set out to do from the very beginning – this was a 21-day alcohol-free challenge, and you won't get the same satisfaction if you don't make it through the whole 21 days. Luckily, there are a few things you can do to ensure you stay in control of your sobriety during these early days.

To begin with, make sure you are realistic about your relationship with alcohol. When you stop drinking, it can be easy to think of alcohol fondly as something you miss and had a lot of good times with. However, when you really pull it apart, this was not your relationship with alcohol at all. If alcohol was good to you and you really did have a great time when you were drinking, you wouldn't have decided to do the 21-day challenge in the first place. In truth, alcohol took over your life, caused you embarrassment, increased your anxiety and made life more difficult.

Many people talk about how much of a challenge it is to "give up" alcohol. However, that's entirely the wrong way to look at it. You're not "giving up" anything – you are ridding yourself of a toxic enemy that you are better off without. Whenever you find yourself starting to think of alcohol fondly and how much you miss it, look back on what you wrote down before you stopped drinking. Relive your darkest times and remember the person that alcohol turned you into. It shouldn't be long before you come to realize that alcohol is by no means your friend, and you're certainly not missing out on anything.

Tips For Staying Strong On Day Four

By your fourth alcohol-free day, you may start to see some semblance of a routine develop. You will likely still be tired and sleeping poorly, but hopefully, you are getting used to the sound of your alarm clock in the morning, incorporating extra fruits and vegetables into your diet, exercising when you feel able, and looking after yourself as best you can. Remember, you have come this far, you have passed the worst of the physical symptoms, and it can only get easier from this point onwards.

If you are hit by a strong urge to pour yourself a drink, there are a few things you can do to combat this feeling. Firstly, remember the reasons you decided to quit in the first place. If you can't always carry around the notes you wrote discussing your reasons for giving up alcohol, consider taking a photo of it and storing it on your phone, or emailing yourself, so that you always have access to your reasons for quitting. These are the most powerful motivators you could wish to have to keep you on your alcohol-free track.

Another option you have when the thoughts of pouring a drink creep into your mind is to mull it over with a friend. Simply discussing how you feel with someone close to you can help make you feel better by unburdening yourself from some of the intense emotions you are experiencing. As well as the therapeutic nature of getting your thoughts and feelings off your chest, discussing your situation with a person you trust allows you to hear their perspective too. They will no doubt be supportive of your decision and have some words of encouragement to keep you motivated through the tougher times of the challenge.

Although many friends would never mention it unless asked or prompted, it is also possible that they can share stories with you of things you have done or said while you were drinking, that you may not remember. Hearing these stories from someone else is more difficult than reliving them yourself – nobody wants to be reminded of their most embarrassing moments by someone else, especially someone they respect. Hearing your friends speak about your actions this way can act as a highly motivating wake-up call, and help get you back on track when you are struggling through the more difficult days of your sobriety.

Of course, it's completely fine if you aren't yet comfortable discussing your sobriety with a friend. This is still all very new for you, and you may not be emotionally ready to speak about it. If you don't want to seek the help of someone else when things start to get tough, it's fine just to ride out the experience as best you can. Watch movies, read books, exercise and just try to distract yourself. Accept that it's hard – you knew it would be. Instead of fighting the feeling and wanting to feel good all the time, learn to accept that you first have to feel worse for a period of time before you can start to feel better. Embrace this, and just ride out the wave, knowing that soon the tide will turn and you'll feel like a new person.

How To Approach Your First Alcohol-Free Weekend

Assuming you started this challenge at the beginning of the week, day five means that you are rapidly approaching your first alcohol-free weekend. You must first take a moment to pat yourself on the back – five days sober is a huge achievement and a great platform from which you can build off and take things even further. However, your first weekend is a dangerous time, and you need to remember that you're still not quite in control of your relationship with alcohol. Don't let this first weekend get the better of you.

One of the key steps to making it through your first sober weekend (and hopefully many more to come), is to remove yourself from the people in your life who you regularly drink with. Firing your drinking buddies might seem like the first thing you should do when the challenge starts, but it's not that simple. You are making a lot of changes at once and need time to put all the pieces of the sobriety puzzle together. With the weekend approaching, now is the perfect time to assess your social life and ask yourself who your friends really are, and who you just hang out with as an excuse to grab a few drinks.

If you come to realize that you only spend time with certain people because you drink together, it may be time for you to distance yourself and let these individuals drift out of your social circle. Chances are, if you are now sober and you don't have anything else in common with them, it would happen sooner or later anyway, but there's no harm in speeding up the process in order to protect your sobriety. This may well be one of the most difficult things you do on your entire 21-day journey, but it is also very important. You don't have to formally let these people know you no longer want to spend time with them, but politely decline their happy hour invitations and don't initiate any plans to spend time together if you know it will inevitably involve alcohol.

It's important to remember that this is a new phase of your life and you are a different person now. Typically, new life phases result in the shuffling around of friends and acquaintances. As we grow and change, so do our values, and it is important that the people in your social group share at least some of those values. Spend more time with the people in your life who don't drink heavily, and focus on activities and events that don't involve alcohol. Friends are a very important part of our mental and emotional health, so make sure you don't simply cut yourself off from having a social life.

It can be difficult to make new friends as an adult, particularly if you are removing yourself from social situations involving alcohol. One of the best ways to meet new people is through the friends you already have. Be open to new activities, and be willing to let your friends introduce you to their other friends. Expanding your network this way means you'll never feel alone and isolated, and it can also be very refreshing to surround yourself with new people when you are trying to shake the reputation of "the one who drinks a lot". These people don't know your past or the silly things you have done when drunk. It's a great opportunity for you to reinvent yourself and start a new and improved chapter of your life.

Another great trick to help you survive your first sober weekend is, believe it or not, to play bartender for yourself. Find some fun and exciting alcohol-free cocktail (mocktail) recipes and get mixing. Mocktails can be just as delicious as their alcohol-containing cousins and can be as simple or as complicated as you choose to make them. One of the features of a good cocktail is that you can't taste the alcohol in it, so with a delicious mocktail in your hand, you won't even notice that you're not drinking alcohol! Recreate virgin versions of your favorite cocktails and see if you can even taste the difference. It's a great way to relax, unwind and treat yourself over the weekend.

Making high-quality mocktails requires high-quality ingredients, so you may want to invest in some good juices and essences. Buying quality ingredients can be expensive, but when you think of all the money you're saving by not drinking alcohol, it's a relatively minor expense and one that's definitely worth it so that you can create delicious alcohol-free drinks. Kicking back on a Saturday afternoon with a mocktail in hand will help you realize that not too much has actually changed in your life. This alcohol-free lifestyle doesn't have to be difficult or change who you are or the things that you enjoy. If you love the taste of an Old Fashioned, you can still have it! Just without the hangover.

Perfecting mocktail making can be quite the hobby to throw yourself into. You'll soon start to see how difficult it can be to balance flavors, and how much skill and science is involved, just as with cocktail making. Once you've got a repertoire of delicious mocktails up your sleeve, why not invite some friends over for a few "drinks" and show off your mixing skills. You'll enjoy spending time and laughing with your friends, and it won't be long before you realize you don't need alcohol to have a good time. Waking up after a dinner party with friends and not having a hangover will quickly become one of your favorite feelings.

Weekends are likely the time when you would usually spend the most money on alcohol. Between stocking up at the liquor store and ordering drinks at bars, alcohol was probably costing you a lot more than you realized. Drinks at bars quickly add up, especially when you are drinking heavily and regularly throughout the entire weekend. Even keeping your fridge or bar cart well stocked is an expensive undertaking. You'll be amazed by how much money you start saving when you give up alcohol. Use your first alcohol-free weekend as an opportunity to reward yourself for the progress you have made so far.

This is a great time to start a "sober wallet". It can be an actual wallet, or a jar or a box. Whenever you think about buying a bottle or hitting the bar for a drinking session, transfer the amount of money you would normally spend into your sober wallet. If you would usually stop on your way home after work to pick up a handle of gin, instead, transfer the money to your sober wallet and watch it grow! You will be shocked by how quickly your money builds up; it will be a great incentive for you to quit drinking for good.

While there are a lot of benefits to giving up alcohol, many of them are difficult to see or measure, or it takes a long time before you can see them. The money that you are saving is one benefit you can see instantly, so it's a good idea to focus on this and use it as a motivating factor to stay sober. Rewards and positive reinforcement we can see have a much more powerful effect on the brain than slow-release rewards such as weight loss or feeling better in the morning, which take longer to show and aren't as easy to measure.

Make sure you use some of the money you are saving to buy yourself a little treat or reward. You can use the money on some healthy stress release activities to help you unwind after your first alcohol-free week. Why not treat yourself to a massage, or really relax and have a spa day. You'll feel great sweating toxins out in the sauna, and a massage will make your healthy new skin feel and look even better than it already was. If you're feeling more active, why not try your first yoga class? The health benefits of yoga are extensive, and most people feel both relaxed and also exhausted (in a good way) afterward. Yoga is a great activity that could become part of your daily routine – replace those evening sessions at your local bar with a yoga session at your local studio. Try a class and see whether or not you like it.

As well as treating yourself to activities, buy yourself something to remember your first week of sobriety with. Maybe you need some new kitchen supplies now that you are cooking healthy meals more often. Or perhaps you should treat yourself to a new pair of running shoes now that you are more active. Even if it's just something small, like a new book or DVD box set, it's good to have something physical that represents the progress of your first week and the success you have had up to this point.

What You Can Expect To See After Seven Alcohol-Free Days

You should feel a huge sense of achievement at the end of your first week of sobriety. This will by far be the most challenging week, and you have shown great strength of character and willpower to make it through your first seven days. Pat yourself on the back! It may seem like a small achievement in the grand scheme of things, but the impact that it could have on the rest of your life is anything but small. You are starting an exciting new chapter in your life, one that is full of promise and possibilities.

The seven-day mark is also an important milestone because it might be when you start to see some physical changes from giving up alcohol. This is exciting because it will inspire you to keep going, and also means that your body is healing and appreciating the effects of an alcohol-free lifestyle. Everyone reacts differently, of course, so it's hard to know exactly when you will start to see these changes, but here is an approximate idea of what to expect after seven days of sobriety.

One of the first changes you may see is with your skin. Alcohol is notoriously bad for your skin, with some studies even finding a link between heavy drinking and an increased risk of skin cancer[18]. Additionally, one study showed that twins who avoided excessive alcohol intake had a younger perceived age than those who did not[28], providing further evidence that alcohol plays a role in the aging of skin cells. Heavy alcohol consumption can lead to visibly older looking skin, as well as skin with a blotchy appearance due to damaged blood vessels. It only takes a week of an alcohol-free lifestyle to allow your skin to rehydrate and recover. Your capillaries will re-form, your skin will start to receive the nutrients it needs, and you'll immediately start to notice your skin looking healthier.

If you've been drinking heavily for a long time, it's possible that some of the damage to your skin, such as premature aging and the increased risk of skin cancer, may be irreversible. However, the longer you maintain an alcohol-free lifestyle, the better the chances of your skin making a marked recovery. Seeing your healthy, smooth, glowing skin will likely provide a huge self-esteem boost and encourage you to continue your alcohol-free journey.

As well as improvements in your skin complexion,

you may start to notice other changes in your face and body. It may only take 1-2 weeks of sobriety until you feel you are starting to lose weight, and you might notice it in your face first. Often, this initial slimming effect isn't actually a result of weight loss but occurs due to sobriety nonetheless. When you drink alcohol, you become dehydrated. As your body realizes it is becoming dehydrated, your cells are instructed to retain all the water they can, because who knows when more fluids will enter your system. This water retention leads to a bloating appearance that is often most recognizable in the face[32].

By removing alcohol from your diet and replacing it with water, you will no longer experience dehydration, and your cells no longer need to hoard water in preparation for a long drought. This reduces bloating and leads to a slimmer looking face. You may notice it when you smile – your cheekbones and jawline will be more defined. You'll also start to notice slimming in the rest of the body, as it is a phenomenon that affects skin cells everywhere. Your weight may not change in the first week of your alcohol-free challenge, but you will certainly appear and feel slimmer. What's more, if you keep up the hard work, it will only be a matter of time before you do start to see significant weight loss.

It's not just physical changes that you can expect to see after your first successful alcohol-free week. You may also notice that your concentration and memory are starting to show signs of improvement[27]. You may find yourself more focused at work, which will definitely have a positive effect on your productivity. Your memory will start to improve the longer you stay sober, which will make it easier to do your job and significantly improve your work output. The fact that these improvements occur so quickly once you remove alcohol from your diet shows how damaging the drug really can be for your brain, and should act as another powerful motivator for you to continue your sobriety journey.

If you are tempted to pull up a seat at the bar during your first alcohol-free weekend, focus on all these positive changes instead. You are already much more in control of your actions and your body; it would be such a shame to return to those out-of-control ways. Remember how one drink would so often to lead to 8 or 9, and how you would turn into a completely different person the more alcohol-fueled you became. You have moved on from being that person; there's no reason to feel that alcohol will always be in control of you. You may always be an alcoholic, but there's no reason why you can't be a happy, sober, and well-adjusted alcoholic for the rest of your life. Don't lose sight of this goal as you enter your second alcohol-free week.

6. Tips For Thriving During Your Second Alcohol-Free Week

You've made it to the beginning of your second alcohol-free week – what an achievement! Think back to six months earlier, did you ever think you'd be able to go this long without alcohol? It should give you a great feeling of satisfaction and help you realize that you are strong and can do anything you put your mind to. You've taken on an incredible challenge, knowing that it would be one of the most difficult things you do in your entire life, and you've already made it through the hardest part! By following the tips and hints in this chapter, you should be able to make it through your second week of the challenge without too many difficulties.

Understanding Alcohol Detoxification During Your Second Week

Full alcohol detoxification can take up to two weeks,

so don't be surprised if you're still experiencing some withdrawal symptoms during your second alcohol-free week. The drug is still working its way out of your system, which takes time and can also result in some unpleasant sensations and prolonged withdrawal symptoms. Despite not yet feeling at your best, you'll feel significantly better than you did during your heavy drinking days. Even though it will be challenging, you'll be able to see that you have made the right choice and your path forward will always be clear. Hang in there!

One common symptom of alcohol withdrawal that lingers into the second week is headaches. It is perfectly normal (if a little frustrating) to experience these headaches for up to a month after you stop drinking[25]. These are nothing to worry about, though you may want to consider taking painkillers if the constant throbbing is getting old. Ensure you are drinking plenty of water, and exercise outdoors when you can. Reducing the amount of time you spend in front of a screen may also help, though it can be challenging to achieve this if you work with a computer all day. Try to read when you get home, rather than watch TV, as prolonged screen time could worsen your headache. If your headaches progress into more than just a dull ache or distract you from working, consult your doctor to make sure everything is okay.

How To Combat Sleep Disturbances During Week Two

Another common week two symptom is disrupted sleep. You might experience insomnia, irregular sleeping habits, and restlessness well into your second week of sobriety, due to the effect that alcohol has on our ability to sleep. Typically, there are three stages of sleep – the first stage is light sleep where you are barely asleep, or just drifting off. The second stage is rapid eye movement (REM) sleep where you dream, and the third stage is deep sleep. Usually, we enter deep sleep naturally from REM sleep, and it is the most important and refreshing stage of sleep.

Ever wondered why you don't feel revitalized after a nap? It's typically because you aren't asleep long enough to make it into a deep sleep. The rest can still help your body, but it isn't the same as a proper deep sleep cycle.

When you drink alcohol, you skip the first two stages and immediately enter deep sleep (otherwise known as "passing out"). Although it may feel like you are sleeping well, this phase of deep sleep doesn't last long – you're back in REM sleep before you know it. This explains how you can still feel so tired after passing out and "sleeping" for hours after a big night of drinking. When you remove alcohol from your diet, your body must re-learn how to fall asleep. With all the other changes that are going on, this can take some time. It can be very frustrating to lie awake at night feeling restless and not being able to do anything about it, but there isn't much you can do about it. Waking up tired is always difficult too, but you just need to remember that these sleep disturbances will eventually pass, and once you adjust to the lack of alcohol in your diet, you'll be sleeping better than ever. If you find yourself really struggling due to lack of sleep, there are natural remedies you can try, such as melatonin, valerian root and magnesium.

Some people also experience nightmares as a result of alcohol withdrawal[22]. Because alcohol lures the body back into REM sleep (which is the phase of sleep when dreaming occurs), you are much more likely to experience dreams and nightmares after drinking. This holds true for the withdrawal phase too, though it is unclear why this is the case. The good news is that these nightmares are only temporary. Once the levels of neurotransmitters in your brain have stabilized, your sleep should be much more consistent, and your nightmares should ease and eventually disappear. Some people find the nightmares unbearable and return to drinking as a way to make them stop. Just remember that they will only be temporary, and once you beat the nightmares, you have beaten alcohol for good.

As well as fatigue from lack of sleep, you may also experience reduced energy levels and changes to your metabolism. Your decreased energy may be partly due to lack of sleep, as well as other changes that your body is going through at this time. Changes to your metabolism may result in noticeable changes in body temperature or appetite. This is all a normal product of your body adjusting to sobriety. Although you won't feel great, at least you have the knowledge that the alcohol is working its way out of your system and it won't be too long before you're feeling better than you ever have before.

Understanding The Emotional Side Effects Of Alcohol Withdrawal

It's important to realize that it's not just physical symptoms you will be experiencing during your second week of alcohol detoxification. It's perfectly normal for your mood to be all over the place –

alcohol has huge effects on the mind, so of course, when you remove it, the mental and emotional effects are profound. Ride the highs and lows as best you can, know that it is only temporary, and reach out to someone whenever you feel as though you need to. Exercise can be a powerful friend and help to stabilize your mood, and of course, having people around that you feel comfortable talking to and confiding in is very important.

Two of the most common emotional side effects of alcohol withdrawal are depression and anxiety[26]. Feelings of anxiousness may begin within a few hours of your last drink and may last for several weeks. Many people think that drinking helps their anxiety, but in fact, in a majority of cases, it is actually drinking that causes anxiety in the first place. Once you have given yourself a chance to undergo a complete detoxification, you will probably find that your anxiety starts to subside. Of course, many people, unfortunately, suffer from anxiety regardless of whether or not they are drinking. If you are one of these people, you can try to lessen your anxiety by eating well, exercising, and ensuring you spend ample time outdoors. Anti-anxiety medications may also help – don't be afraid to discuss this option with your doctor.

Depression is a very common side effect among people who give up alcohol. Like nightmares and anxiety, this too, is caused by an imbalance of neurotransmitters that occurs as your brain tries to adjust to the absence of alcohol[19]. As with anxiety, many people believe that drinking keeps their depression at bay, or at least helps them to forget about it. Once again, this is usually not the case. Depression is a symptom of alcohol dependence, and once you rid yourself of alcohol, you may find that your depressive symptoms improve significantly.

Often, we become depressed due to aspects of our lives that we feel we cannot control. Instead of relying on alcohol and losing even more control over your life, wave goodbye to alcohol and take charge of your circumstances. Use your momentum from kicking alcohol as a platform to change other elements of your life that you aren't satisfied with. Create a list of things you wish were different, separate out the ones you have the power to change, and get to work becoming the best possible version of yourself. Of course, it's not always this easy, and some people just naturally feel depressed. Make sure you always know where to find help when you need it, and never feel ashamed or embarrassed to speak with your doctor about depression.

During your second week of alcohol withdrawal, you may also experience increased feelings of aggression or hostility. This is a direct result of the brain's hyperexcitability that occurs when you immediately remove alcohol from your diet. You may find yourself experiencing road rage when you're normally very placid, or losing your patience with people more easily than you normally would. Increased aggression is normal and should subside with time like the rest of your alcohol withdrawal symptoms. Similarly, some people experience changes to their sex drive following alcohol withdrawal. You may experience a decreased sex drive or a general disinterest when it comes to sex, simply because your brain has too many other things to deal with! This, too, should resolve itself over time.

Focusing On The Positives During Week 2

Although it may sound like there's not a lot to look forward to when it comes to your second alcohol-free week, this isn't the case at all! Sure, there will be some side effects to deal with, but at least you're not constantly hungover and regretting your choices from the night before. There are actually a lot of positives that you will start experiencing during your second alcohol-free week, and even more to look forward to as you progress through the challenge. If you are struggling with your sobriety and start to miss alcohol, focus on these positives for some extra motivation. Try to figure out what is driving you the most. Write down your top five reasons for giving up alcohol, and why each one is important to you. If you find yourself getting bogged down in the challenge and need a little motivation, here are some examples of where your sobriety can take you.

One major positive is, of course, all the physical health benefits that come with avoiding alcohol. You lower your risk of heart disease, numerous types of cancer, liver disease, stroke and so much more the moment you stop drinking. You will likely live longer than if you made no changes and proceeded to drink your life away. What's more, you will likely lose weight due to the sheer caloric content of all types of alcohol, as well as the fact that you're probably more likely to snack when you're drinking. By cutting alcohol out of your diet, you will now have bonus calories to spare! This means you can occasionally treat yourself to ice cream, chocolate, cake, or just a snack whenever you feel like it, and probably still lose weight!

Another major benefit is all the money you will be saving. By the end of your second week, your savings will be significant, even if you have been treating yourself and splurging here and there. Chances are, you had no idea how much money you were spending on alcohol until you stopped drinking. A few drinks at the bar add up quickly, as does a trip to the liquor store. Keeping track of the money you have saved is a great motivating force to keep you on track to make it through to your third week of the challenge.

Although it may be a while before it takes effect, sobriety will eventually help improve your sleeping patterns. Once your body has adjusted to the absence of alcohol and your brain is no longer dependent on the drug, your sleep habits will be much healthier. You will stay in a deep sleep longer and wake up feeling well-rested and ready to take on the world. Getting to this point can often feel like quite the challenge; you might be tossing and turning in bed for months before your sleep finally improves.

However, when you do start sleeping well again, you won't believe how much better you feel and how much easier it is to make it through the day.

Many people give up alcohol so that they can become a better partner, friend, parent, or employee. This is a great reason – nobody wants to feel as though they are letting their team down or burdening the ones they love. One of the most important positives of giving up alcohol is that it improves your relationship with the people around you. Your boss and colleagues will notice as you become more reliable and productive. Your friends will feel that you are more invested in them and want to spend quality time together, rather than just using them as an excuse to get drunk. Your partner will love the effort you are making to improve yourself, and the fact that you are taking your health and wellbeing seriously. Using your relationships with other people as a motivating factor can be very powerful – just be sure to remember that you're doing this for yourself, too.

Speaking of yourself, another powerful motivating factor can simply be the sense of self-satisfaction you will have at the end of your challenge. Even at this point, two weeks into the challenge, you must be feeling very proud of your achievements. Imagine how much stronger that feeling will be when you make it to the finish line! Many people complete the 21-day alcohol-free challenge purely to prove to themselves that they can do it and to revel in the immense feeling of self-achievement that comes from successfully making it through the challenge.

Whatever your personal reason, use it as motivation to keep going during the tougher times. Think of all the benefits of sobriety and how they outweigh the benefits of drinking. Drinking might take away your problems in the short term, but it gives you more to deal with in the long term. Sobriety means you will have more money, be in better health, and have better relationships with the people you care about – all amazing benefits that set you up for success in the long term. Keep that in perspective as you push towards the final week of your alcohol-free challenge.

How To Wear Your Sobriety Proudly

Making it to the end of your second week of sobriety is a huge achievement. Not only should you be proud of your efforts, but you should also be vocal about them too. Ensure everyone around you knows you're doing the challenge, and knows how well you're doing. Let them see how good you look, how clear your skin is, and how much weight you've lost. If you're comfortable, share with people why you've embarked on this journey, and what it has meant to you. It will probably be one of the most profound experiences of your life, so don't be afraid to reflect on it regularly.

Be prepared for the fact that many people will want to know about your experiences. Before you gave up drinking, weren't you also curious as to how it would feel? How hard would it be to quit? What would the most challenging aspect be? What is the biggest benefit? Everybody wonders from time to time whether they should take a break from alcohol, and how it would feel, so don't be surprised if you find yourself answering a lot of questions. Don't be afraid to open up to people about your experiences, but only share what you feel comfortable with. Who knows, you might even inspire someone to embark on their own 21-day challenge.

If you need a little extra motivation to finish up week two, why not try to use your sobriety to raise some money for charity? Chances are, before you started the 21-day challenge, you probably had a bit of a reputation for being a heavy drinker (whether you knew it or not). There might be a few people out there who don't think you'll be able to make it through three whole weeks without a drink. Make them put their money where their mouth is by donating a dollar for every day you stay sober. You'll feel even better about yourself and your sobriety if you know you're also helping a good cause.

7. Week Three: The Final Hurdle

You have now entered your third and final week of the 21-day alcohol-free challenge. What an achievement! Take some time to reflect on what this challenge has meant to you, what the struggles have been, and what your greatest victories were. If you could start it all again, what would you do differently? What advice would you have for someone embarking on the challenge for themselves? This will be one of the most intense experiences of your entire life – take a moment or two to appreciate it! It says so much about you as a person that you have been able to make it to this point, and you're so close to the finish line now.

For any moments of weakness or lapses in concentration during your third and final week, remind yourself of how close you are to the end and how far you have come. You didn't set out to complete a 17-day challenge, or a 20-day challenge, and you will most certainly not get the same sense of success if you do all the hard work but then don't make it to the end of the 21 days. You're just a few days away from one of the biggest milestones of your life – don't give up now! Remember that this three-week period may only represent around 0.08% of your life, not a lot of time to sacrifice to sobriety if you think about it. Remember your reasons for embarking on this challenge, and finish strong!

How To Survive Social Events During Your Sobriety

During your third week, you may start to feel as though you are completely in control of alcohol in your life. Hopefully, you have started to love how sobriety feels, and don't actually want to go back to drinking. If you can honestly look yourself in the mirror and say that this is how you feel, great! You may be ready to venture back out into social situations with people who are drinking. You do need to keep in mind that being back in an environment where there is ample alcohol will require a lot of willpower. Until now, you have only had to passively say no to alcohol – by avoiding the liquor store or turning down a happy hour invitation. If you do go out with friends, you will have to avoid alcohol actively. Somebody might ask you what you want to drink or try to buy you a drink. You need to be ready for these situations and be completely sure you can handle them. If there's any doubt at all in your mind, stay away from all situations involving alcohol for the time being.

If you do feel ready to head back to the bar for a pint of water, there are a few things you can do to ensure you don't slip up. The key is in the preparation – make sure you have a foolproof plan for staying sober, and you stick to it. One drink might not seem like a big deal, but it will inevitably lead to more, and you really don't want to wake up regretting your decision and feeling like a failure. Don't make a spontaneous decision to go out with friends on a Friday night after work. Instead, make sure you have had time to come up with a sobriety plan and ensure that you are ready for the challenges of being around alcohol. Below are some of the factors you need to consider when planning to stay sober during a night out.

Firstly, make sure you are driving. Being the designated driver, or at least driving yourself home, is a great way to ensure you stay sober. You know the law and don't want to break it. Plus, it's a matter of safety as just one drink can impair your concentration and reflexes. Make the decision to drive and park in a place where you can't leave your car overnight. This will force you to stick to your plan, stay sober, and get you and your passengers home safely. Be sure to let bar staff know you are the designated driver – sometimes they will offer you free soda or other drinks for your efforts.

As well as putting your hand up to drive, make sure everyone you are with knows you won't be drinking, and haven't been for some time. This will mean that nobody tries to pressure you into drinking with them, or inadvertently buys you a drink and puts it in front of you. If your friends truly are your friends, they will understand and respect your decision. Plus, they will probably love the chance of a free ride home! You don't have to give your reasons for staying sober, but ensure everybody realizes that you want to have a good time without partaking in the libations. Go out, have a good time, and show your friends that you can still be fun even when you're not six drinks deep. If you experience any sort of peer pressure or negativity at all, remove yourself from the situation. You don't need to be around people who will try to encourage you to drink when you have voiced your desire to stay sober.

Don't feel at all embarrassed or self-conscious about telling your friends that you're not drinking at the moment. You have made incredible progress and should be proud of your achievements. Chances are many of them have taken a break from alcohol at one point or another, or wish they could. It is likely that they will be somewhat curious as to your motives, but overall just supportive of your decision. Relax and enjoy your night out with friends – you've earned it. Watch them as the alcohol starts to take effect – you might never have seen it from the perspective of a sober person before. See how quickly it affects their actions and impairs their decisions? That shouldn't be a life you want to go back to. Keep watching them – maybe you will be the one who can retell embarrassing stories the next day for a change!

As further motivation for staying sober, make a point to remember all the positives you have experienced so far during the challenge. You are saving money, you have lost weight, your skin looks and feels great, you have more energy, you are both mentally and physically healthier, your liver is starting to regenerate, and you are finally beginning to feel like you are in control of your relationship with alcohol. Focusing on the positives rather than the negatives will help to show you that you have made the right decision, and might even make you excited about the prospect of a future without alcohol.

Some of the changes, such as improvements in your skin, or weight loss, may have occurred subtly over the challenge. Because you see your reflection every day, it can be difficult to notice these subtle changes as they happen. Take a look at the photo you took of yourself before the challenge began – can you see the difference? You will probably notice it most in your eyes, skin, and the shape of your face. If you don't want to go back to the way you looked before the challenge, don't succumb to a moment of weakness on your first sober night out.

In the unlikely event that you need even more reminding of why drinking is a bad idea, there's a wildcard that we haven't even mentioned yet. Remember your old nemesis, the hangover? Just one drink on your first night out could lead to several more, which would definitely lead to you waking up and feeling truly terrible the next day. Fatigue, a terrible headache, intense nausea, tremors, stomach irritation, severe dehydration, a deep sense of shame and regret, anxiety, and so much more. Basically, all the symptoms that you fought so hard to overcome at the start of the challenge could return instantly if you slip up during your first sober night out. The last thing you need right now is a crippling hangover that could keep you in bed for a day (or even longer) when you have just started to move on from that toxic phase of your life. Remember all the miserable days you wasted in bed with a hangover when you could have been doing something productive? Leave that life where it belongs – in the past.

If you have taken all of the above factors into account and feel certain that you can be around alcohol without giving in to temptation – go for it! However, it is very important to know your limits and to sense when you are not yet ready for this step. Diving into a happy hour before you are ready could have a catastrophic effect on your sobriety, and derail all the hard work you have done and the incredible accomplishments you have made. Everybody has limits; don't be afraid to admit yours. Stay home for a few more weekends until you can be sure that you are in control of your relationship with alcohol.

Reaching The End Of The 21-Day Challenge

Waking up on your last day of this three-week rollercoaster ride can bring with it a huge range of emotions. Hopefully, you are feeling an overarching sense of pride – you have achieved what probably seemed like an impossible task just one month earlier. You should be thrilled with the progress you have made and the changes you have seen, both physical and emotional. You have ridden the highs and lows, learned a lot about yourself, and come to understand how strong you can be when you put your mind to something. Make sure you take a photo of yourself to compare to your "before" photo – the differences you see will be astonishing!

Once you have completed the three-week challenge, you need to decide how you will proceed. Although surviving without alcohol for 21 days is a huge achievement, don't ruin the mental victory by diving straight back into alcohol the moment the challenge is over. You should have been able to show yourself that you don't need alcohol in your life, you don't miss it, and you don't crave it anymore. Hopefully, the three-week challenge has helped to reset your relationship with alcohol. Why not prove this to yourself by completing another week of the challenge? If you completed three alcohol-free weeks, there's no reason why you shouldn't be able to complete four – it will be your easiest week yet!

It's a good idea to check in with your doctor at the end of the three-week challenge, especially if you are still experiencing any side effects. By this stage, you should be mostly side effect free, with the possible exception of lingering sleep disturbances. Of course, the severity and duration of the side effects you experience also depends on how much alcohol you were consuming prior to the challenge. If you are still experiencing side effects, this may be another reason to wait one more week before you reintroduce alcohol into your life.

Alternatively, maybe you feel better than you ever have and have made the decision to continue with your sobriety. This is fantastic! Without the 21-day challenge, you never would have known about the benefits of a life without alcohol, and now you are living them for yourself. Staying sober is a great idea if you are at all worried about losing control or "relapsing" into alcoholism the second you pour your first drink. For many people, not drinking at all is actually easier than drinking a small amount, as one drink can so easily lead to many more. If you fall into this category, persist with your sobriety. After all, you've learned that life without alcohol isn't so bad, right?

It is important to realize that you may never have a normal or healthy relationship with alcohol. It is a mind-altering substance and has profound effects on our behavior and emotions. If you do bring alcohol back into your life, learn from your past mistakes, know when to stop, and return to sobriety as soon as you feel yourself losing control. You can't "cure" alcoholism – it's more important to manage the condition as best you can and know the difference between healthy and unhealthy drinking. If you think you can manage your relationship with alcohol and contain yourself to drinking in moderation, following the tips in the next chapter will allow you to do just that.

8. How To Manage Your Relationship With Alcohol And Drink In Moderation

If you do decide to reintroduce alcohol into your life, you need to be very careful with when and how you do this. Make sure that your decision is predetermined – don't simply go to the bar without a plan, or buy a bottle of liquor and bring it home without thinking the decision through. Instead, decide on exactly which day you will have your first drink, decide what it will be, and decide how much alcohol you will allow yourself. If you are wondering how much alcohol is a "safe" amount to consume, you can follow the CDC guidelines – 11 drinks per week for women, 17 drinks per week for men. When you are just easing yourself back into alcohol consumption, it's best to start with much lower numbers than these.

Sit down with a calendar and plan out exactly on which days you will drink, and which days you will not. For the first month, allow yourself three days per week where you consume alcohol and don't drink on the remaining four days. In that month, allocate one weekend where you will refrain from alcohol. It is important to do this so that you have a set plan to stick to, and so that you remember that you can still enjoy life when you are not drinking. Having regular alcohol-free days will ensure that your body and mind don't come to depend or rely on alcohol. Stick very tightly to these goals, and if you notice yourself starting to crave alcohol, stop drinking for the remainder of the month.

As well as setting goals to keep track of your drinking, make sure you count and record your drinks. Start a spreadsheet or just a written note about what you drink and when, and add in the cost of the drink so you can keep track of how much money you are spending on alcohol. If you can see right in front of you just how much money you are spending on alcohol, you may be encouraged to drink less. Similarly, write down why you want to limit your drinking, and write a reminder of how good you felt during the 21-day challenge when you weren't drinking. Even though you are occasionally drinking again, don't lose sight of the fact that alcohol is not your friend! Remember all the dark times when you overindulged, and how long it took both your body and your mind to recover from the heavy drinking sessions. If you come to rely on alcohol again, you will have to repeat the whole detoxification, and we both know you don't want to do that. Stick to your drinking schedule, and keep yourself in check.

There is no point tracking how much you are drinking and limiting yourself to 1-2 drinks per day if you are not carefully measuring the volume of alcohol you are consuming. If you are making drinks at home, make sure you measure them and follow the CDC guidelines for what constitutes a "standard drink". From the CDC guidelines, one glass of wine is a 5oz pour, so make sure you stick to this volume and don't fill up your glass. Invest in a wine stopper to keep opened bottles of wine fresh. If you are making cocktails or mixed drinks, only include a 1.5-oz shot of liquor. For beer, one standard drink is 12-oz, so if you go to the bar and order a 16-oz pint, be mindful that you are consuming more than one drink according to the CDC guidelines. Instead, order a smaller pour – most bars have a 10 or 12-oz option that tastes just as good!

Food is a very important factor when it comes to controlling your drinking. Make sure that you always eat within 30 minutes of any alcohol consumption, as having food in your stomach will slow down the effects of alcohol intoxication. You probably already know from past experiences that if you drink alcohol on an empty stomach, it can hit you much faster. The concern here is that you will have one drink, feel a nice buzz, and decide to order another one. This is where you can find yourself in trouble – how many times have you woken up with a hangover and known you got out of control because you hadn't eaten anything? Eating food may also help to reduce your craving for alcohol, and will make you feel full so that you don't drink as quickly.

When you first begin to reintroduce alcohol into your life, make sure you keep yourself away from situations where you would normally drink a lot. If there was a particular happy hour that you used to attend with your friends and have four or five drinks, don't go. If you have a certain group of friends who are your "drinking buddies", distance yourself from them or limit the amount of time you spend together. You are still in a delicate phase of recovery, and maintaining a healthy relationship with alcohol needs to be your number one priority. People, places, objects, and activities can all be triggers that would normally cause you to crave a drink (or several). Try to identify your triggers and write them down, so that you know which situations to try to avoid.

If you feel a void in your life that alcohol used to fill, find something else to fill it with! This is a very exciting notion – you are now free in the evenings and on weekends and will have lots of spare time for new activities. Take up a hobby or a sport, or join a MeetUp group to make new friends who don't see drinking alcohol as a priority. You can also spend more time with your family, who will love being around this new and improved version of you. Use the extra time you have in the evenings for cooking delicious and nutritious meals or start an exercise regime. If you always thought you couldn't afford a gym membership, this will definitely have changed with all the money you are saving on alcohol. These are all activities that are better for both your mind and your body than alcohol will ever be.

Chances are, you learned how to say "no" during the 21-day challenge. You will need to continue to do this as you reintroduce alcohol into your life. Make sure you are comfortable saying no before you put yourself in any social situations involving alcohol. It won't be too long before someone offers you a drink, or expects you to drink with them as you have in the past. Tell your friends and family that you are trying to limit your alcohol consumption so that they don't put any pressure on you to share a drink with them. It's not only other people you need to say no to – make sure you can say no to yourself and stop drinking when you know you've had enough.

Embracing The Benefits Of The 21-Day Challenge

Whether or not you decide to drink alcohol again after the 21-day alcohol-free challenge, there's no denying that the experience itself is life-changing. A taste of the sober life can open your eyes to its benefits and help you discover that you want to make the change permanent, or it can simply fill you with the reassurance that you can stop drinking when you put your mind to it. However, when you're not used to it a life of sobriety can seem very intimidating. Many people worry about becoming bored, not having fun and losing their friends. While sobriety is not without its challenges, the benefits far outweigh the downsides.

The short-term benefits of sobriety are all fairly obvious; no crippling hangovers, no embarrassing texts, no stories from your friends about the stupid things you did, no blacking out, and putting yourself in potentially dangerous situations that you don't even remember. The long-term benefits of sobriety can be less obvious but are usually more significant. These are the meaningful, life-changing benefits that stick with you for years after you make the decision to pursue sobriety or limit your alcohol consumption. Whenever you find yourself craving a drink or missing the presence of alcohol, remember these long-term benefits of your life-changing decision, and how much better off you are now.

Now that you've done all the hard work and you're seeing the benefits of your efforts, it's important to make the most of the benefits and really reap the rewards of the challenge. It is one thing to simply notice that you have saved money, or lost weight, but these benefits don't really take their full shape until you utilize them, by putting yourself out there and showing off the effects that the 21-day alcohol-free challenge had on you. At the end of the challenge, make sure you take some time to focus on how you will take advantage of all the benefits of the challenge.

When it comes to sobriety, one of the most drastic changes you will notice is the amount of money you save. Even if you do go back to drinking occasionally, you will not be spending anywhere near as much money on alcohol as you were prior to the challenge. Why not come up with a plan for your savings? Keep track of approximately how much money you are saving, and think of a goal to put it towards. You may even want to transfer a set amount every week (however much you used to waste on alcohol) to a separate account. Plan for a long-term goal like a vacation, a new car, or even a house down-payment. This will be a great long-term motivator to keep you on a positive track to maintaining your sobriety.

Of course, the health benefits of sobriety or reduced drinking should not be overlooked. Studies have shown that sustained sobriety can lead to liver regeneration and restoration of function[4]. This means that some of the liver damage you have given yourself from heavy drinking can actually be reversed when you stop drinking. Each day you are still drinking is a day you are missing out on a chance to start improving your liver function. What more incentive could you possibly need to help you decide that the time is ripe to give up alcohol?

As well as these obvious benefits, there are some more subtle benefits to sobriety that you may not even consider until they hit you. Of course, everyone has a different journey and different experiences along the way, so the biggest benefit of your own sobriety could be completely different to the person next to you. That's exciting though, isn't it? You don't even know what the best part of your journey will be until you reach the end of it! So, now that your three weeks are up, what was your biggest, unexpected highlight? Make sure you take time to reflect on this, and if you ever feel as though you are losing control, think back to how things were, and how important this positive change has been in your life.

Many parents who do the 21-day alcohol-free challenge are surprised that one of the major changes they experience is an improved relationship with their children. Without the thought of alcohol to preoccupy the mind, these parents are more engaged with their kids, form closer bonds, and enjoy a rewarding emotional experience that greatly benefits both parent and child. If you've ever been hungover around a toddler, you'll know all too well that it's impossible to match their energy levels and shudder at the thought of their high-pitched squeals. When you're sober, healthy, and happy, you have the ability to keep up with them, play games, love and nurture them, and overall show up and make the most of their all too brief childhood.

The hugely important mental health benefits of sobriety should not be overlooked. If you are one of the many anxiety sufferers who experience greatly improved and reduced symptoms after giving up alcohol – embrace it! If you've always been too anxious to join a club or a sport, now is the time to challenge yourself and see what you are really made of. Making new friends and putting yourself in unfamiliar social situations as an adult is hard, and it's even harder when you're sober. However, you've just been through one of the toughest experiences of your life – now is not the time to be beaten by anxiety. Don't let it stop you from signing up for that indoor soccer team, or enrolling in a pottery class.

If you used alcohol as a coping mechanism to deal with stress, anxiety, or hardships, sobriety forces you to find other ways to deal with these circumstances. This is an important life skill to have and will make you more prepared for the inevitable ups and downs of life. Alcohol is never the solution to your problems – it is a way of avoiding them and can even create more problems for you in the long term. By using alcohol as a coping mechanism, you never make the changes you need to be content, and end up in a cycle of dissatisfaction. Give up alcohol and find real solutions to your problems instead.

It should be easy to see that the benefits of sobriety clearly outweigh any downsides. In the immediate moment when you are caught up in the vicious cycle of alcohol abuse, sobriety never seems like the answer. But when you really pick it apart and start to consider the numerous, significant benefits, the decision to stop drinking is clearly the right move to make.

Conclusion

At some stage, each and every one of us reaches a point where we question how much we are drinking. Does alcohol play too much of a role in our life? Have we inadvertently turned something we enjoy into something we are dependent on? Are we drinking to the point where we are causing our bodies serious, permanent damage? When these questions arise, it's time to reassess our relationship with alcohol. One of the best ways to do this is to make the decision to take a break from drinking. The 21-day alcohol-free challenge is a great way to take a deep breath and make some serious lifestyle changes when it comes to your relationship with alcohol.

Although the thought of 21 days without alcohol might seem overwhelming, the challenge is very achievable if you take it one day at a time. One of the keys to succeeding in the challenge is to plan and prepare for it meticulously. Make sure your reasons for taking on the challenge are clear in your mind, and write them down so you can remind yourself when things get tough. Ensure that you understand how the process of alcohol detoxification works and learn about what to expect when it comes to withdrawal symptoms.

Sure, alcohol is fun and delicious, but it's also incredibly toxic to both our physical and mental health. Excessive alcohol consumption significantly increases our risk of developing numerous diseases and increases levels of anxiety and depression. What's more, it makes us do stupid things that we often end up regretting (if we even remember them), and can seriously affect our relationships with our colleagues, family, and friends. Taking a break from alcohol can help us reassess our priorities, and decide whether the short-term benefits of alcohol are actually worth the damage it can cause to all aspects of our health.

Doing the 21-day alcohol-free challenge does not

mean that you can never enjoy alcohol again. But similarly, it does not mean that you will simply go back to your old habits once the 21 days are up. The challenge helps to reevaluate your relationship with alcohol completely and reset how your brain feels about it. You will no longer be dependent on alcohol, you will be in control of your relationship with alcohol, and you will be able to decide whether or not you wish to reintroduce alcohol into your life after this point.

Ultimately, the 21-day challenge is about much more than your relationship with alcohol. It is physically and mentally challenging, and will be one of the most difficult tasks you perform in your whole life. It is an excellent opportunity to learn more about yourself and how you deal with things when the going gets tough. People who successfully complete the challenge experience an incredibly strong sense of achievement, which translates positively when they decide to take on other challenges. You will learn a lot about yourself and what you are made of when you give up alcohol for 21 days.

Life is already short, don't waste your time being hungover and regretting every Saturday night. Find out how life feels without alcohol and see what you're made of by taking on the 21-day alcohol-free challenge.

References

1. Arias-Carrión, Ó., & Pöppel, E. (2007). Dopamine, learning, and reward-seeking behavior. *Acta neurobiologiae experimentalis.*

2. Barbaccia, M. L., Affricano, D., Trabucchi, M., Purdy, R. H., Colombo, G., Agabio, R., & Gessa, G. L. (1999). Ethanol markedly increases "GABAergic" neurosteroids in alcohol-preferring rats. *European journal of pharmacology, 384*(2-3), R1-R2.

3. Bayard, M., Mcintyre, J., Hill, K. R., & Woodside Jr, J. (2004). Alcohol withdrawal syndrome. *American family physician, 69*(6).

4. Bouneva, I., Abou-Assi, S., Heuman, D. M., & Mihas, A. A. (2003). Alcoholic liver disease. *Hospital Physician, 39*(10), 31-38.

5. Brower, K. J. (2003). Insomnia, alcoholism and relapse. *Sleep medicine reviews*, *7*(6), 523-539.

6. Bruha, R., Dvorak, K., & Petrtyl, J. (2012). Alcoholic liver disease. *World journal of hepatology*, *4*(3), 81.

7. Carr, A. (2003). *The easy way to control alcohol* (3rd ed.). London, UK: Arcturus Publishing Limited.

8. de Visser, R. O., Robinson, E., & Bond, R. (2016). Voluntary temporary abstinence from alcohol during "Dry January" and subsequent alcohol use. *Health Psychology*, *35*(3), 281.

9. Edwards, G. (1990). Withdrawal symptoms and alcohol dependence: fruitful mysteries★. *British Journal of Addiction*, *85*(4), 447-461.

10. Foley, T. E., & Fleshner, M. (2008). Neuroplasticity of dopamine circuits after exercise: implications for central fatigue. *Neuromolecular medicine, 10*(2), 67-80.

11. George, D. T., Zerby, A., Noble, S., & Nutt, D. J. (1988). Panic attacks and alcohol withdrawal: Can subjects differentiate the symptoms?. *Biological psychiatry, 24*(2), 240-243.

12. Guiraud, V., Amor, M. B., Mas, J. L., & Touzé, E. (2010). Triggers of ischemic stroke: a systematic review. *Stroke, 41*(11), 2669-2677.

13. Hillers, V. N., & Massey, L. K. (1985). Interrelationships of moderate and high alcohol consumption with diet and health status. *The American journal of clinical nutrition, 41*(2), 356-362.

14. Holmes, M. V., Dale, C. E., Zuccolo, L., Silverwood, R. J., Guo, Y., Ye, Z., ... & Cavadino, A. (2014). Association between alcohol and cardiovascular disease: Mendelian randomisation analysis based on individual participant data. *Bmj*, *349*, g4164.

15. Kelley, A. E., & Berridge, K. C. (2002). The neuroscience of natural rewards: relevance to addictive drugs. *Journal of neuroscience, 22*(9), 3306-3311.

16. Koller, W., O'Hara, R., Dorus, W., & Bauer, J. (1985). Tremor in chronic alcoholism. *Neurology, 35*(11), 1660-1660.

17. Krajka-Kuźniak, V., Paluszczak, J., Szaefer, H., & Baer-Dubowska, W. (2013). Betanin, a beetroot component, induces nuclear factor erythroid-2-related factor 2-mediated expression of detoxifying/antioxidant enzymes in human liver

cell lines. *British Journal of Nutrition*, *110*(12), 2138-2149.

18. Kubo, J. T., Henderson, M. T., Desai, M., Wactawski-Wende, J., Stefanick, M. L., & Tang, J. Y. (2014). Alcohol consumption and risk of melanoma and non-melanoma skin cancer in the Women's Health Initiative. *Cancer Causes & Control*, *25*(1), 1-10.

19. Laine, T. P. J., Ahonen, A., Räsänen, P., & Tiihonen, J. (1999). Dopamine transporter availability and depressive symptoms during alcohol withdrawal. *Psychiatry Research: Neuroimaging*, *90*(3), 153-157.

20. Lieber, C. S. (1989). Alcohol and nutrition; an overview. *Alcohol Health & Research World*, *13*(3), 197-206.

21. Liu, S. W., Lien, M. H., & Fenske, N. A. (2010). The effects of alcohol and drug abuse on the skin. *Clinics in dermatology*, *28*(4), 391-399.

22. Nielsen, T. A., & Zadra, A. (2005). Nightmares and other common dream disturbances. *Principles and practice of sleep medicine*, *4*, 926-935.

23. Pehrson, A. L., & Sanchez, C. (2015). Altered γ-aminobutyric acid neurotransmission in major depressive disorder: a critical review of the supporting evidence and the influence of serotonergic antidepressants. *Drug design, development and therapy*, *9*, 603.

24. Peters, B. L., & Stringham, E. (2006). No booze? You may lose: Why drinkers earn more money than nondrinkers. *Journal of Labor Research*, *27*(3), 411-421.

25. Robinson, S., Meeks, T. W., & Geniza, C. (2014). Which agents work best: FDA approved and off-label medications help patients achieve abstinence and maintain sobriety. *Current Psychiatry*, *13*(1), 22-31.

26. Roelofs, S. M. (1985). Hyperventilation, anxiety, craving for alcohol: a subacute alcohol withdrawal syndrome. *Alcohol*, *2*(3), 501-505.

27. Roseribloom, M. J., Pfefferbaum, A., & Sullivan, E. V. (2004). Recovery of short-term memory and psychomotor speed but not postural stability with long-term sobriety in alcoholic women. *Neuropsychology*, *18*(3), 589.

28. Rowe, D. J., & Guyuron, B. (2010). Environmental and genetic factors in facial aging in twins. *Textbook of Aging Skin*, 441-446.

29. Sachdeva, A., Choudhary, M., & Chandra, M. (2015). Alcohol withdrawal syndrome: benzodiazepines and beyond. *Journal of clinical and diagnostic research: JCDR*, *9*(9), VE01.

30. Sarkar, D., Jung, M. K., & Wang, H. J. (2015). Alcohol and the immune system. *Alcohol research: current reviews*, *37*(2), 153.

31. Schütze, M., Boeing, H., Pischon, T., Rehm, J., Kehoe, T., Gmel, G., ... & Clavel-Chapelon, F. (2011). Alcohol attributable burden of incidence of cancer in eight European countries based on results from prospective cohort study. *Bmj*, *342*, d1584.

32. Skinner, H. A., Holt, S., Sheu, W. J., & Israel, Y. (1986). Clinical versus laboratory detection of

alcohol abuse: the alcohol clinical index. *Br Med J (Clin Res Ed)*, *292*(6537), 1703-1708.

33. Weiss, F., Lorang, M. T., Bloom, F. E., & Koob, G. F. (1993). Oral alcohol self-administration stimulates dopamine release in the rat nucleus accumbens: genetic and motivational determinants. *Journal of Pharmacology and Experimental Therapeutics*, *267*(1), 250-258.

34. Wilson, C., & Moulton, B. (2010). Loneliness among older adults: A national survey of adults 45+. *Washington, DC: AARP.*

Disclaimer

The information contained in this book and its components, is meant to serve as a comprehensive collection of strategies that the author of this book has done research about. Summaries, strategies, tips and tricks are only recommendations by the author, and reading this book will not guarantee that one's results will exactly mirror the author's results.

The author of this book has made all reasonable efforts to provide current and accurate information for the readers of this book. The author and its associates will not be held liable for any unintentional errors or omissions that may be found.

The material in the book may include information by third-parties. Third-party materials comprise of opinions expressed by their owners. As such, the author of this book does not assume responsibility or liability for any third-party material or opinions.

whatsoever without the written expressed and signed permission from the author.

Milton Keynes UK
Ingram Content Group UK Ltd.
UKHW041313300924
1924UKWH00034B/144